THE BRITISH INTERNAL-COMBUSTION LOCOMOTIVE:
1894-1940

David & Charles Locomotive Studies

Locomotive Monographs

General Editor:

O. S. Nock, BSc, CEng, FICE, FIMechE

DAVID & CHARLES LOCOMOTIVE STUDIES

THE BRITISH INTERNAL-COMBUSTION LOCOMOTIVE: 1894-1940

BRIAN WEBB

DAVID & CHARLES : NEWTON ABBOT

0 7153 6115 5

To my parents who have cheerfully borne for many years the relics and literature of their railway enthusiast son, and also to Sandra, who edited, typed and generally made readable the manuscript on which this book is based

Set in ten on eleven point Plantin
and printed in Great Britain
by W J Holman Limited Dawlish
for David & Charles (Holdings) Limited
South Devon House Newton Abbot Devon

CONTENTS

INTRODUCTION

THE story of the internal-combustion locomotive has been recounted in part many times and in numerous publications, usually with an emphasis on continental and American practice that suggests little British participation in this and the internal-combustion engine's history. This representation of continental practice as having been the most advanced is not warranted for British work in this field was just as important and, one may claim, more advanced in some respects.

In the course of surveying the British contribution to the development of internal-combustion rail traction a tremendous amount of work by British engineers and inventors has been discovered, and to cover all of it in detail in one volume is not possible. This survey of a largely unprobed field of British railway work is, therefore, restricted to locomotive work during the period 1894-1940, and an attempt has been made to present the more interesting and important work of these years in a readable manner.

The omission of much technical information is intentional, for this is readily available in many cases in contemporary technical publications. The absence of full technical descriptions of some of the locomotives mentioned is due to lack of the necessary information at the time of going to press and the writer would welcome any additional details which readers may be able to contribute.

BRIAN WEBB

CHAPTER 1

THE ORIGIN OF THE INTERNAL-COMBUSTION ENGINE

THE story of the development of the internal-combustion engine is a long, involved, and most interesting one, but as it would fill a book on its own it is not the intention here to examine it at any great length. Some indication of the vast amount of work carried out is, however, appropriate, together with a survey of some points of special importance.

Today we have the internal-combustion engine or petrol engine, plus a derivative operating on paraffin (kerosene), both being called either a petrol engine or a paraffin engine because of the fuel on which they operate. In addition, we have the compression-ignition engine which operates on heavy fuel oil and which is popularly referred to as the 'Diesel' engine. Oddly so, perhaps, since we do not call a steam engine a 'Watt' engine, and as will be seen, the development of the compression-ignition or heavy fuel-oil engine was not due solely to the work of any one man.

To clarify the difference between these three engine types we can summarise as follows:

Petrol engines. In this form of engine the fuel is petrol which is mixed with air to form an explosive mixture. This is then exploded by an electric spark while under compression in the engine cylinder.

Paraffin engines. The fuel in this case is light oil or kerosene, originally called heavy oil. The fuel is first vaporised by heat, then sprayed into the engine cylinder where it is in contact with air compressed by the piston and an explosion takes place.

Heavy fuel oil engines-Compression-ignition engine. This is a combustion engine in which air is sufficiently highly compressed to enable it to ignite the fuel oil which is introduced at very high pressure in a pulverised state at the top of the cylinder, the ignition of the oil-air mixture driving the engine piston.

Numerous references are available as to the exact working cycles of these engines and, as with their history, any good technical library can provide a far more complete account than is possible here.

Hundreds of people—inventors, engineers, scientists, mathematicians—were involved over as many years and the summary presented here covers only some of them and their work.

The first applications of the principles of internal combustion were made, as is well known, by Hero, who about 200BC in Alexandria devised a form of steam turbine. There is no doubt that he understood the principles he employed; or that about 2,000 years later, Charles Parsons, while working at the Kitson works at Leeds, rediscovered it, as too did the Swedish engineer, De Laval.

One early use of the principles of internal combustion was, of course, the development of gunpowder and guns, for when gunpowder was exploded in the barrel of a cannon containing a projectile, the projectile was forced out at great velocity.

About 1678 Abbé Hautefuille described an engine used for pumping water, which apparently worked by using the partial vacuum resulting from the exploding of gunpowder in a cylinder. Needless to say, the idea did not prosper, the failure to find a way of controlling the amount of gunpowder used each time proving fatal in more ways than one!

In 1794 Robert Street of Christchurch, in Hampshire, patented an internal-combustion engine consisting of a cylinder and a piston. The bottom of the cylinder was heated by a fire and the engine operated by pumping in small quantities of turpentine or similar distillate which was vaporised by the heat of the fire. The piston was then raised slightly by a lever which sucked in air and ignition took place, thereby raising the piston. This was

9

probably the first use of the hot-bulb type vaporiser.

In France, Philip Lebon patented during 1801 a gas engine in which gas was compressed in a separate cylinder before being admitted into the working cylinder. Lebon's patent mentions the use of an air-pump for compressing atmospheric air and also an electric spark for ignition. But for his early death, internal-combustion engines might have been used commercially much earlier than they were.

In 1833 L. W. Wright of London took out a patent for an internal-combustion engine. This engine received two impulses for every revolution of the crankshaft and with a pump compressed the air and gas prior to admission to the working cylinder. Water cooling was employed and the engine had cam-type exhaust valves, but it aroused little interest at a time when engineers were pre-occupied with the steam engine.

William Barnett of Brighton patented a two-cycle internal-combustion engine in 1838. The patent also proposed both double- and single-acting engines. Here again the mixture was to be pre-compressed prior to being fed into the working cylinder. A number of these engines were built and were the ancestors of the two-cycle internal-combustion engine with gear-operated gas- and air-pumps. It seems possible, in spite of many inventors' claims, that Barnett really was the first to use the two-cycle double-acting system.

Stuart Perry worked on a somewhat similar engine to Wright's, designed to burn liquid hydrocarbon fuels mixed with air, which was heated by exhaust gases. Perry's engine was both double-acting and reversing. Hot-tube ignition was proposed, although this again was a 're-invention' (remember Robert Street in 1794, Newton in London in 1855 and Drake in the USA).

Two Italians, Eugenio Barsanti and Felice Matteuci, took out a British patent in 1857 for a free piston-type design of engine, with a vacuum. The explosion forced up the piston free from the connecting rod, the work being carried out in the fall of the piston whose weight, and the atmospheric pressure, pushed it down into the vacuum left by the explosion. Later in the 1860s Hugon worked on a similar engine.

J. J. E. Lenoir in France patented an engine in the 1860s which was a big improvement on previous work in that it used an inflammable mixture of gas and air ignited by electricity. The rise and fall of the piston was used to drive a crankshaft, and it had separate inlet and outlet ports. The use by Lenoir of sparking-plugs was a great step forward and the Lenoir engine went into production commercially both in France and England. It was killed, however, largely by prejudiced reports and the commercial interests behind steam engines, plus some badly-handled newspaper reports and adverse publicity.

At the 1867 Paris Exhibition the work of Otto and Langen was shown in the form of an internal-combustion engine of the free-piston type, being very similar to the work of Sir Samuel Brown in England in the 1820s and 1830s, and that of Barsanti and Matteuci in 1857. Otto and Langen developed it and made it into a successful commercial engine; it still used flame ignition.

Nikolaus August Otto continued his work by following on the ideas of Lenoir, using a crankshaft-type engine with electrical ignition. He later became interested in the compression engine and his patent licensees in England, Crossley Brothers, did much useful development work on it. Otto's four-stroke engine of the mid-1870s, soon known as the 'Otto Cycle' engine, followed the researches of the Frenchman, Beau de Rochas, who in 1862 patented a compression engine on which almost all future work was to be based. Points made by Beau de Rochas included the use of the largest cylinder volume, the charge to be compressed by the return of the piston from the previous stroke as quickly as possible. The ignition of the fuel charge should take place at dead centre, allowing expansion during the third working stroke, exhausting the burnt gases during the last or fourth stroke.

Sir Douglas Clerk 're-invented' and patented a two-stroke cycle engine in 1881.

Karl Benz patented a crude form of carburettor in 1886 and is also incorrectly credited with inventing the electrical spark ignition system.

James Brayton of Boston, USA, contributed much useful thought on gas engines, on fuel injection and on the constant pressure engine.

Gottlieb Daimler in 1882 left Otto's company to open his own business and in 1883 patented the first high-speed petroleum engine, though it contained few innovations. Nevertheless, history owes much to his firm faith in the high-speed lightweight internal-combustion engine and he soon had engines in service running at up to 900rpm.

Rudolph Diesel, born 18 March 1858, took no early part in the history of the internal-combustion engine for, as we shall see in the next chapter, both Priestman and Akroyd Stuart were proving their engines' commercial viability by the time Diesel took out his first patents. Although the principles of compression-ignition were correctly set out some seventy years previously by Sadi Carnot, Diesel applied for his first patents for Germany and other countries in 1892, but sold them the following year to a laboratory jointly operated by Maschinenfabrik Augsburg-Nürnberg Co (MAN), and Krupps of Essen.

Rudolph Diesel aimed at producing an engine in which very high temperatures and pressures would ensure maximum efficiency and low fuel consumption, while at the same time developing a higher horsepower than any other engine. In his first patent of 27 February 1892 the first two points clearly state the principle he alone set out: (i) avoid mixing the air and the fuel—or only air to be inducted; (ii) the combustion air to be compressed high above levels previously used so that the compression temperature rises far above the fuel ignition temperature. His work failed to make progress largely because of the general belief, shared by scientists and professors alike, that Sadi Carnot's system of a constant temperature combustion cycle was the one for all future compression-ignition work, and even Diesel's patent included Carnot's system—so much was it considered the acme at that period.

Why Diesel's second patent of 6 April 1892 did not repeat the two cardinal points already mentioned is a matter for conjecture, but the effect was to make everyone think that he was adopting Carnot's system throughout this very difficult development period. Meanwhile, Diesel had seen his mistake and changed to his constant pressure combustion cycle, unfortunately without publicly announcing this. It may have been that he did not wish to make the Carnot protagonists, some of whom were good friends of his, look foolish but, whatever the reason, the subsequent general knowledge that the change had been made appears to have been the main cause of the discredit which so affected his work. Diesel pulled out of the work in 1898 leaving it to MAN to carry on the production of a viable engine, though not without many departures from Diesel's original conception. The support of Heinrich von Buz, Joseph Vogt and Emanuel Lauster must be noted as being most important during the struggles to evolve something of commercial value from the foundations Diesel had laid for MAN. The work at MAN centred on liquid fuels, and experimental engines were built using heavy fuel oil, but little progress was made. There was much rethinking of ideas which resulted in the adoption of features Diesel had hoped not to use, such as water-jacketed cylinders.

At the same time a number of other firms were licensed by MAN to build engines, including Sulzer Brothers and Deutz on the Continent and Mirrlees & Watson in Glasgow, some soon giving up in desperation, although work in Glasgow did achieve successes.

During 1897 MAN completed a 20hp engine which was built and tested with some success but not without great expense to the MAN and Krupp organisations. The following year an engine was built and sold for stationary industrial use, this reviving the interest of the licensees, who also resumed their work.

In principle the MAN-Diesel heavy fuel oil engines were compression-ignition in operation, employing the temperature of highly compressed air in the engine cylinder to explode the oil which, in a pulverised form, was fed into the cylinder by a blast of compressed air; this followed upon the work of the Frenchman, Emil Capitaine. Today the fuel-injection system is by solid injection or airless injection, the air oil blast having been dropped.

It was perhaps his vision of the heavy fuel oil engine revolutionising transport and power production, rather than the development of his own engine, which makes Rudolph Diesel stand out. Before 1900, he had foreseen the coming of the high-powered railway locomotive we know today. This is seen in the 1912 locomotive collaboration with Sulzers, Adolph Klose, and Borsigs which is discussed later. His work with Adolph Saurer at Arbon, dating from 1907-8, produced the first fast-running compression-ignition engines, and although only of some 30hp, they ran at 800rpm. His premature death in September 1913, when he was lost overboard from the Antwerp-Harwich steamer, was unfortunate, and but for this it is likely that rail traction would have shown greater progress at an earlier period.

The bulk and weight of engines of higher power presented considerable problems to locomotive manufacturers and, coupled with the problem of transmissions and a limited range of materials, restricted the use of the heavy fuel oil engine for many years. It was not, however, generally realised that lower engine weights and the provision of flexible transmissions was a premium for rail traction. The result was that much work was done on locomotives with direct drive and reversible engines, which were started by means of compressed air in the same engine.

The first internal-combustion locomotive was the Daimler-powered unit of 1890. This two-axle low-powered unit, and the later Priestman and Hornsby-Akroyd Stuart oil-engined locomotives of 1894-1902, were also all of low power, although the Hornsby locomotives were commercially successful. Transmission flexibility, after the various abortive attempts with direct-drive, compressed air and such like, was seen as desirable though obviously not a problem to be easily resolved.

Engine work continued with Atlas and ASEA in Sweden and Sulzer in Switzerland, all of whom had engines in railway applications by 1920. In Germany, Maybach, as a result of their wartime work with light petrol engines for aviation use, turned their attention to the compression-ignition system and set about building a heavy fuel oil engine and a Maybach transmission to go with it, both of which were applied to a railcar in 1923. MAN, too, were similarly engaged on the lightweight fast-running theme but mainly for road transport. The successful MAN submarine engine was available for railway use, and though its size limited its use in any numbers, it worked well in its few applications.

It was now that British work in the field of rail traction-engines really began to come to the fore. Concentration of interest on the lightweight, fast-running, high-power engine coincided with the work of Robert Bosch in Germany and that of Alan Chorlton in the United Kingdom. Chorlton had done work on aviation engines and it was the evolution of his form of airless fuel-injection pump and fuel system which marked the real turning point. He worked with the Beardmore group at Glasgow to produce the range of Beardmore compression-ignition engines which owed nothing to any other engine range in production for rail traction purposes. From 1925 onwards, the Beardmore engine gained a reputation second to none throughout the world.

This engine found many applications in all forms of rail traction duty but, apart from a few engines used in shunters and railcars, was sadly neglected in the home market. Impressive service figures were built up in various applications of the engines overseas but the apparent inability of locomotive manufacturers to appreciate the possibilities of building a lightweight mechanical structure to take advantage of the Beardmore engine largely killed the engine. Engines exported to Canada, for example, were used in the Canadian National Railways 290-ton 2-Do-1 and 1-Do-2 monstrosity. This, with an installed horsepower of 2,660hp (from two Beardmore 1,330hp engines weighing 42 tons) required a further 248 tons for

the mechanical portion, transmission and auxiliaries, fuel, etc—hardly a serious commercial proposition. The suggestion is that the builders of this unit, well-established steam and straight electric locomotive builders, were doing their best to dispel any idea that locomotives of this type could ever constitute any kind of challenge.

The consortium which built the locomotive was the Canadian Locomotive Co Ltd, using Baldwin locomotive works' drawings under the supervision of the Westinghouse Electric Co Ltd, who worked closely with Baldwins and occupied an adjoining plant. Baldwins themselves had already gained a reputation for heavyweight oil-electric locomotives such as the Baldwin-Knusden 120-tonner, and it was much the same policy that forced them out of business some thirty-five years later when their unwieldly work had been proved uncompetitive.

The Beardmore engine was without doubt before its time. It was built in powers ranging from 90hp to a V-form 12-cylinder, 1,330hp unit. All the engines were well designed and light in weight, with running speeds initially of 800-900rpm, although by the early 1930s a 1,200rpm engine was being offered. In 1934, at a time of financial pressure, the Beardmore group decided to cease engine manufacture and though this was only a small part of the group's activities, it was most unfortunate that this decision should have been taken just when interest was beginning to be shown in such advanced engines as theirs.

Up to 1930, transmissions for rail traction were still restricted in the main to mechanical types for the low-powered locomotives and electrical transmissions for the higher powers. Although it was twenty-five years since Herman Föttinger had taken out his first patents and various derivatives of his work were being developed, it was not until J. M. Voith of Heidenheim, Germany, took a serious interest after 1930 that any real success with locomotive hydraulic transmissions was attained. Similarly, Föttinger's work provided the basis for the fluid coupling with which Harold Sinclair was so successful in the United Kingdom from 1930, especially in conjunction with the Wilson epicyclic gearbox, and these found ever increasing use. Variations of hydraulic transmissions using hydrokinetic, hydrostatic and hydromechanical systems were under development in Europe and, following Voith, it was the Maybach–Mekydro (also traceable to Föttinger's work) which became popular.

Alfred Lysholm and Jan Smith developed the Lysholm-Smith torque converter and their licensees produced variations under the names of Twin Disc, Krupp, SRM, and in the United Kingdom by Leyland, Vickers, and Coats.

Hydrostatic transmissions were worked on by both Hans Thoma and George Constantinesco, but while derivatives of Thoma's line of thought were produced by Lentz, Williams-Janney, Haslam & Newton, and Badoni, Constantinesco's perserverence with his mass-inertia ratchet drive transmission unfortunately met with little success, largely because of technical problems with materials, ratchet sizes, design and strength. The British hydrostatic pioneer, Professor Hele-Shaw,

had taken out his patent in 1908 and, as we shall see, his was the first hydraulic transmission to be successfully applied in rail traction.

Other research work on transmissions included compressed-air systems by Dunlop and also Hautier, compressed gas by Schelest and also Zarlatti, the latter trying compressed steam, as did Cristiani. Direct drive was tried by Borsig-Sulzer-Klose-Diesel, Leroux, Ansaldo, Deutz, and diesel-steam was tried by Kitsons. The transmission story is a particularly interesting one, but, unfortunately, it is not possible to develop it further here.

CHAPTER 2

THE FIRST OIL-ENGINED LOCOMOTIVE

LEAVING the general story of the oil engine and its evolution we can now turn to the British field where thought was already being directed towards application of the oil engine in transport, while other countries were still trying to build commercial engines.

Sir Frederick Bramwell, at a meeting of the British Association in 1881, said that the steam engine, no matter how much loved and cherished, would become, in its reciprocating form at any rate, a thing of the past in about fifty years' time. Although a little out with his timing, his prophecy has been proved correct, and even within his fifty years' limit the writing was already on the wall.

That same year, 1881, Eugène Etève and Charles Clément Lallement of Paris patented their 'improved motive-power engine operated on hydro-carburetted air', and it was this engine, exhibited in London, which prompted a Yorkshireman, William Dent Priestman of Hull, to take up the manufacture of a similar engine at his Holderness foundry. Priestman's thoughts had been running in this direction for some time, and he had first announced his intention of producing such an engine in 1879.

His first engines were gasoline engines following on the patents of Etève and Lallement and the principles of Lenoir. These were horizontal engines giving a power stroke at each revolution of the crankshaft, but he was not at all satisfied and took out a licence from Crossley Brothers to use the four-stroke system, the patent of which did not expire in the United Kingdom until 1890. Several engines were built and tested but, owing to the highly volatile petroleum fuels, met with little success. Priestman, therefore, decided to embark on an engine of his own design which would operate on a less dangerous fuel, kerosene or heavy oil. This idea was not new since patents had been taken out for this type of engine, but the kerosene, due to its oily nature, tended to carbonise quickly,

causing fuel-admission problems which seemed insurmountable. Efficient combustion of the fuel in the cylinder, and a solution to the problems of atomisation, were the first objectives tackled by Priestman. By inventing his oil sprayer after many failures and over two years' work, and by using a heated chamber to vaporise the fuel prior to injection, he achieved success. The oil sprayer involved a jet of oil passing through a fine opening and being met at almost right angles by a stream of air, the pre-heated oil being sprayed into the engine cylinder which contained air compressed by the piston. The fuel was then ignited by an electric spark, so giving the power stroke. A patent of 1872 by Brayton describes a method of fuel atomisation and injection by compressed air in conjunction with a petroleum engine.

Priestman continued his research work and built one engine to operate at higher compression, but after several mishaps the experiments in raising compression ceased. Although not carried to the full extent at which compression temperature alone would ignite the fuel (in this case heavier oils than paraffin), his experiments, he no doubt hoped, would achieve this and did indeed cause the 'knock' so familiar in the Diesel engine today.

The main point about Priestman is that he patented his engine in 1885. By 1888 he was actually selling his engines commercially for industrial applications, replacing steam engines. Soon they were installed in collieries as pumping- and hauling-engines, driving machinery, generators, compressors, barges, ships, etc, and by the time the first diesel engine was being experimented with in 1898 in Germany in its first industrial application, 100hp Priestman engines of vertical four-cycle double-acting types were being used in ships. The first diesel engine to be put into a ship was a 20hp horizontal four-cycle type for a barge in 1903.

In 1888 the Priestman oil engine was awarded the Silver Medal of the Royal Agricultural Society

Fig 1 *The world's first oil-engined locomotive of 1894, built by Priestman Brothers Ltd of Hull*

at Nottingham, and from then up to 1895 something like 1,000 Priestman engines were placed in service; one in 1894 had been installed in a railway locomotive, the first oil-engine locomotive in the world. Four years earlier, in 1890, Daimler had built a 4hp petrol unit on the continent, but this low-powered unit was not a success and it was the Priestman unit with the oil engine which is the true ancestor of our heavy fuel oil-engined locomotives of today.

The Priestman locomotive was a small four-wheel unit of standard gauge with a flat-topped, wagon-like underframe with the engine mounted transversely on top under an overall canopy roof supported by four corner pillars. The engine was a vertical twin-cylinder unit of the 12hp marine type, running at 300rpm and driving to a crankshaft with a large flywheel at one end on the side of the locomotive frame.

After trials at the Priestman works it was taken to the Alexandra Dock of the Hull & Barnsley Railway at Hull, where it was demonstrated from time to time on shunting duties. Its success was limited because its low power output restricted its haulage capacity to one loaded wagon at a time. Though before its time, this locomotive was unique in railway practice in having a double-acting oil

engine and, like the 8hp Priestman lorry of 1897, the important place it deserves in transport history is still largely unrecognised. The Priestman locomotive is shown in Fig 1.

At the same time as Priestman was working at Hull, a fellow Yorkshireman, Herbert Akroyd Stuart, was busy at Fenny Stratford, in Buckinghamshire. Born at Halifax on 28 January 1864 (Priestman was born at Sutton, near Hull, 23 August 1847), Stuart arrived on the scene during a period of intense activity in internal-combustion engine development, for it was during this decade that the engine began to emerge as a commercial and practical proposition.

Stuart's early work was carried out at his father's factory in Fenny Stratford and he took out his first patent for an oil engine on 5 November 1890. This was a true oil engine and up to a dozen appear to have been built at Fenny Stratford by 1891. A few others were built in London during the same period but it was not until the patents were acquired by Richard Hornsby & Sons Ltd of Grantham that the full potential of Stuart's engine was realised. For this, credit is due to the foresight of the chief engineer at Hornsby's, R. E. Edwards, who despite considerable opposition, persuaded Hornsby's to go ahead and purchase the engine.

As was to be expected, the first engine work at Grantham met with problems, particularly in piston design, and the blow-past troubles gained some notoriety for the shop where the engines were tested because of the clouds of black oily mist usually present! However, perseverance eventually paid off and in due course over 32,000 Stuart engines were built and sold. The first Hornsby-Akroyd engine was sold in 1892 for stationary use at the Great Brickhill Waterworks, Fenny Stratford. This engine, which later saw use elsewhere, was eventually given recognition and exhibited in 1930 at the British Industries Fair before finally returning for restoration in 1939 to Grantham, where it is now preserved at the works there. Herbert Akroyd Stuart died on 19 February 1927 at Claremont, Western Australia, and is buried in his native county, at All Souls Church, Halifax.

The work of Priestman, followed by that of Akroyd Stuart, was the true basis of the heavy oil engine as we know it today. Stuart introduced the feature of fuel injection into the air near the end of the compression stroke, ignition taking place by the heat of compression. He used a vaporiser to vaporise the fuel and so allow for ignition at a moderate degree of compression. He used airless injection equipment and also an antechamber, the forerunner of the modern pre-combustion chamber. Akroyd Stuart was not, of course, the first to realise the possibilities of compression-ignition, but he was the first to build an engine of this type and, with the interest and progressive outlook of Richard Hornsby & Sons Ltd, to make a real success of it in practical applications.

For over seventy years Germany has popularly been acclaimed as the birthplace of the compression-ignition engine but, in fact, the modern high-compression engine of today owes more to British thought than to Diesel's and, especially, to those pioneers, Priestman and Akroyd Stuart. Priestman was the first to suggest admitting the fuel to the air charge after compression and it was only when Stuart was prevented from making the 'diesel' engine by troubles with fuel injection that he resorted to the pre-chamber as a substitute.

It is, however, convenient in this work to continue to refer to the engine as the 'diesel' engine and so avoid such unwieldy descriptions as 'compression-ignition mechanical', 'compression-ignition electric', for 'diesel mechanical' or 'diesel electric', or such accepted abbreviations as 'dm' and 'de'.

CHAPTER 3

THE FIRST COMMERCIAL LOCOMOTIVES

IT was Richard Hornsby & Sons Ltd of Spittlegate Ironworks, Grantham, who built the first commercially successful oil-engined locomotives, and between 1896 and 1903 six locomotives of four different types were manufactured, all powered by the Hornsby–Akroyd patent oil engine. All six locomotives were built to meet special government and military requirements.

The first example was Hornsby works No 1705 and it was delivered on 23 July 1896 to the superintendent of building works for use at Woolwich Arsenal. This two-axle locomotive of 18in gauge was powered by a Hornsby–Akroyd 9½hp engine with one single horizontal cylinder with a bore of 11in and a stroke of 15in. The engine was placed over the trailing axle just in front of the driving position and drove onto a transverse shaft with a large flywheel at each end set above the locomotive frame. The transmission was via a train of gears, including reverse, to a jackshaft in front of the leading axle and slightly above, with side-rod drive to the rear or trailing axle; hand brake only was fitted. There was at the front end of the locomotive a tall cylindrical water tank into which the engine exhausted, so giving an effective flameproof exhaust 'quenching' system before release into the atmosphere. The locomotive had a wheelbase of 3ft 6in and wheels of 20in diameter.

Between 1900 and 1902 three more locomotives were built, of very similar design to No 1705. To obtain steadier running, frame length was increased to allow for the addition of a leading pony truck (thus giving them the 2–4–0 or 1–B axle arrangement) which was placed 5ft in front of the leading driving axle. The pony-truck wheels were of the same diameter as the driving wheels, 20in. The rigid wheelbase was 3ft 6in and total wheelbase was 8ft 6in. Apart from this modification, they were all identical to the 1896 locomotive and were delivered to Woolwich Arsenal as follows: locomotive 4535 on 11 May 1900; 5242 on 15 May 1901; and 5883 on 11 March 1902. All of these locomotives were employed in the arsenal's explosives factory, their only fault being that they were somewhat underpowered for the work they were required to do.

Fig 2 *The Hornsby–Akroyd engined unit of May 1900, a 2–4–0 of 18in gauge built by Richard Hornsby & Sons for Woolwich Arsenal*

17

THE BRITISH INTERNAL-COMBUSTION LOCOMOTIVE: 1894–1940

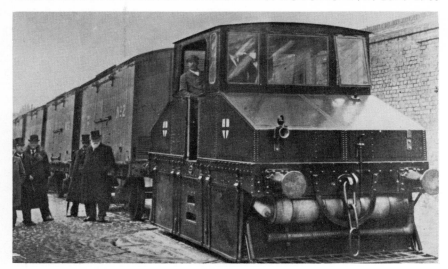

Fig 3 *The solitary 80hp Maudslay machine of 1902 for Deptford Cattle Market*

Fig 4 *Richmond Main Sewerage Board's 7hp Blake unit of 1903 (2ft 9in gauge)*

Hornsbys were not traditional locomotive builders, for this was their only locomotive work, and their example was quickly followed by other non-traditionalists, this time road-vehicle manufacturers. The Maudslay Motor Co Ltd of Coventry built, or supplied (for it is not certain that they actually constructed the mechanical portion), a quite large shunting locomotive of standard gauge for use at the Deptford Cattle Market of the City of London Corporation in 1902. Resembling contemporary electric locomotive practice in that it had a centre cab with sloping bonnets or housings at each end, it was obviously intended to work over rails set in roadways, similar to tram tracks, and had side covers over the wheels and a fender beneath the

bufferbeam at each end in tram locomotive fashion. Running on two axles, it had a Maudslay three-cylinder vertical petrol engine with 9in × 9in cylinders giving 80hp at 450rpm; an 8hp petrol starting engine was also fitted. Little is known of the transmission, which was of the two-speed type, but a load of 60 tons could be hauled on the level.

By way of contrast, the next locomotive to appear was a very diminutive machine indeed and was built by F. C. Blake & Co Ltd of Kew, Surrey, who were established as engine makers for various motorcar firms and also built cars of their own design in small numbers. Built by Blakes to meet the requirements of William Fairley, it was delivered in November 1902 to the Richmond Main

Sewerage Board, Mortlake, for use on their 2ft 9in-gauge light tramway system. The locomotive replaced horse traction on the line and handled about 250 tons of dried sludge cake each week between the works and the private dock on the Thames. It was said to have operated at a fuel cost of 8s 0d per week.

Of simple but robust construction with a steel channel underframe, it had a Blake two-cylinder vertical engine of 7hp driving via a cone-type clutch and constant-mesh gearbox. Final drive was from a countershaft by roller chains to each axle. Weighing 16cwt in full working order, it had speeds of 3 and 7mph.

On 14 January 1903 another Hornsby–Akroyd engined locomotive was delivered. This one, works No 6234, did not go to Woolwich Arsenal but, according to surviving records, to the inspector of iron structures at Chatham Dockyard, for use on the 2ft 6in gauge Chattenden & Upnor Railway. This design was a considerable advance on the Woolwich quartet, being carried on two six-wheel bogies giving an axle arrangement of C–C. This 20hp unit had a horizontal single-cylinder engine of 9¾in bore and 10in stroke containing two opposed pistons. The engine cylinder was over the rear bogie just in front of the driving position. The front piston drove onto a crankshaft running between bearings in the centre of the locomotive. The rear piston connected to a crosshead at the rear of the cylinder, which was in turn connected by two long rods to a further crosshead placed over the trailing wheel of the front bogie. Two connecting rods then drove the same central crankshaft. Drive was through a two-speed and reverse gearing to a central lay shaft running across the locomotive under the crankshaft, from which, through bevel gears, two propeller shafts drove the rear axle of the rear bogie and the front axle of the leading bogie, the three axles of each bogie being rod-coupled. The bogies had wheels of 16in diameter and a wheelbase of 1ft 9in, the speed range being 2½ and 7mph.

The Wolseley Tool & Motor Co Ltd, Birmingham, another road vehicle maker, built a few petrol-engined locomotives about 1903–4, some of which were interesting designs, but as Wolseleys did not consider there was sufficient demand for such locomotives their interest in this field soon died. Wolseleys were also reputed to have stated that they did not consider there was a future for the internal-combustion engine in rail traction.

One of their designs was a 1ft 6in gauge two-axle petrol locomotive built in 1903 for use underground in South African gold mines, one of the first underground locomotives ever built. It was powered by a Wolseley horizontal two-cylinder engine of 18hp, running at 600rpm. The trans-

Fig 5 *The opposed-piston engined Hornsby C–C locomotive of 1903 for the Chattenden & Upnor Railway (2ft 6in gauge)*

R9827

mission included a cone clutch of the friction type formed inside the engine flywheel. This drove to the transverse shaft of the three-speed gearbox by chain. The transverse shaft carried a bevel wheel reverse gear, driving through the sliding gear shaft by positive clutches. Most interesting of all was the final drive which was by cardan shaft to both axles. The overall length was 11ft, wheelbase 4ft 6in, wheel diameter 18in, speeds being 4, 8 and 15mph.

The last locomotive built at Grantham by Hornsby & Sons was delivered on 16 January 1904 to the inspector of iron structures, Chatham, for use on the 2ft 6in gauge Chattenden & Upnor line. Following upon the twin-bogie locomotive of 1903, it also had the same type of opposed piston engine. The engine drove to a crankshaft across the centre of the locomotive, which drove through an idler gear to the jackshaft, which in turn ran in front of the coupled wheels; the power output was 15hp. The mechanical portion, however, followed that of the final three Woolwich Arsenal units and had the 1–B axle arrangement; its speed range was 5 and 8mph. Although this was the final Hornsby unit, others were designed and a 1910 diagram has come to light showing a 45hp two-axle unit with a vertical four-cylinder in-line engine and jackshaft drive.

Another Wolseley locomotive was a 2ft 9½in gauge petrol unit of the 0–4–0 type, built in 1904 for service at a 'north of England works', as yet untraced. It had a similar engine to the 1903 mining locomotive and the transmission included a two-speed and reverse gearbox giving 3 and 8mph. In working order it weighed 3 tons, its wheels had a diameter of 18in and its maximum drawbar pull was 1,000lb.

Although they had only recently opened their own works, Kerr Stuart & Co Ltd had been in business many years as suppliers of railway equipment, using sub-contractors to build their products. After purchase of the California Works at Stoke-on-Trent it was not long before they were thinking of internal-combustion locomotives for light railways and one was put in hand in October 1903. Kerr Stuart's first petrol locomotive, works No 860 of 1904, was delivered in February of that year to Sekondi Ashanti Goldfields Ltd, Ashanti. Described by the manufacturer as 'an open type locomotive', it was an 0–4–0 type with a steel girder-type underframe, an overall roof with four corner supports and seats at each end (the first double-cab internal combustion locomotive?). The engine and transmission were exposed and comprised a Gardner two-

cylinder vertical engine of 25hp. The transmission drove to a jackshaft unit across the locomotive at one end mounted on top of the underframe. Circular section rods drove the wheels, which had coupling rods. The locomotive weighed 2 tons 12 cwt in working order; overall length was 11ft 2in, overall height 6ft 2in, overall width 3ft 7in, wheelbase 3ft 7in, wheel diameter 20in.

A similar locomotive, ordered for stock in January 1904, was works No 861. This had the same engine and transmission arrangement but was shorter and had a seat at the jackshaft drive end only. It weighed 2 tons 11cwt in working order, had an overall length of 9ft 9in, overall height of 6ft 2in, width of 3ft 7in, wheelbase of 4ft and wheel diameter of 18in. Although of the canopied open type, it had a bonnet over the engine. It was sold and delivered to Welsh Crown Spelter Co Ltd, Treffriw, North Wales, in April 1904, but was soon out of use when the mine closed shortly afterwards.

Kerr Stuart built two more petrol locomotives during 1905 which were very similar to locomotives 860/1. A similar underframe was also used, a one-end cab arrangement as on 861, but the whole engine was enclosed by a full-width bonnet and the driver had a substantial cab. Described as the 'enclosed type', they were both 0–4–0 type units of 2ft 6in gauge and had, as in the case of locomotives 860/1, a Gardner No 3 HV two-cylinder vertical kerosene engine, but rated at 12–14hp at 700rpm. A similar transmission with final jackshaft drive on top of the underframe was employed. The first locomotive (KS 887) was delivered in May 1905 to the Morvi State Railway, India. Weighing 2 tons 3cwt, it was 10ft in overall length, 10ft 7¼in in height, with a wheelbase of 3ft and wheel diameter of 18in; the starting tractive effort was 600lb. The second (KS 930) was delivered via agents, (F. S. Greenshields & Co Ltd,) to Wellington, New Zealand, for a mysterious purchaser, in September 1905. This little locomotive may have worked on White Island, the crater of a volcano off the east coast of North Island, which had a small works and tramway, set up to collect and refine the sulphur. However, an eruption appears to have wiped out the operation shortly after the locomotive's arrival.

During 1905 and 1906 two firms who were to enjoy much success with internal-combustion-engined rail vehicles started in business. One of these was McEwan Pratt & Co Ltd, with an office in London and a works, the Murray works, at Wickford, Essex. This firm became world famous for its products during its relatively short

Fig 6 *The first Kerr Stuart petrol locomotive, KS 860, for Sekondi Ashanti Goldfields Ltd in 1904 (18in gauge)*

span of activity. The other firm was founded by Mr J. Drewry, who opened a small works at Teddington under the name of The Drewry Car Co Ltd to make petrol rail trolleys and inspection cars, a development from an earlier family business for the construction of road vehicles. Drewry products were sold by A. G. Evans & Co of London and the Teddington works had produced some 200 vehicles by the time it closed in 1908. It appears that Drewrys used petrol engines mainly of BSA manufacture in its rail vehicles, hence its link with that firm after 1908.

McEwan Pratt soon built up, as did Drewry, an excellent reputation throughout the world for their petrol-engined vehicles and railway equipment. McEwan Pratt's range included rail tractors of all sizes, locomotives, petrol trolleys, railcars, and rolling stock, mainly for light railways and plantation lines. Their rail tractors were typified by their tall centre cab, prominent external cooling radiators and chain-drive transmissions. It seems that a range of small petrol engines, the Murray, was also made at Wickford and was used in their products, though this is not entirely certain. A typical McEwan Pratt rail tractor, exported to Java in 1907 for plantation use is, shown in Fig 7.

Fig 7 *A typical plantation locomotive by the Wickford works of McEwan Pratt, supplied to Java in 1907*

It was probably after the start of the acquaintance of Drewry with Ernest E. Baguley that Drewry closed his Teddington works and transferred the manufacture of his products to the Small Heath works of the Birmingham Small Arms Co Ltd in 1909.

Ernest E. Baguley, a figure not to be underrated in the history of non-steam rail traction, was born in 1863 and subsequently became chief draughtsman at W. G. Bagnall Ltd, Stafford. He left this firm in 1902 to pursue his growing interest in road vehicles and became manager of the Rykneild Engine Co Ltd, road vehicle manufacturers, at Burton-on-Trent. Baguley designed the works and planned the layout of the buildings for Rykneilds, and when he left them in 1907 it was to take up an appointment with the car division of BSA at Small Heath. It was here that Baguley probably first came in contact with the Drewry Car Co Ltd, the beginning of a long association of the two names.

Due, it is thought, to a change in policy at BSA, Baguley left them in 1911, up to which time he had been responsible for the manufacture of Drewry's rail vehicles, an arrangement which terminated at BSA in early 1912. This will be developed later in the story.

One of the largest locomotives built at Wickford by McEwan Pratt & Co was sold in 1909 for service with the Assam Oil Co Ltd, Assam. This substantial centre-cab locomotive of the 0–6–0 type was a metre-gauge petrol unit and had a four-cylinder 50hp engine which was started by a Murray patent starting-gear to the magneto. The transmission had a multiple-disc dry clutch and a two-speed gearbox giving $4\frac{1}{2}$ and 10mph; final drive was by chain, with axles coupled by side rods. Weight in working order was $7\frac{1}{2}$ tons, or 9 tons when ballasted, and it could haul 67 tons at 10mph.

McEwan Pratt had always been beset by financial difficulties and, although operations commenced in 1905–6, the company was not incorporated until 1909. The near bankrupt state, from which the company was saved by mortgaging the works and by loans from the directors, did not, however, detract from the quality or advanced nature of their products, particularly their railcars which, unfortunately, are beyond the scope of this work.

W. J. Bassett Lowke Ltd of Northampton, the renowned model engineers, who had gained prominence as builders of miniature steam locomotives, built, in 1909, the very first steam locomotive to have an internal-combustion engine. This use of a steam locomotive design to hide a petrol engine and transmission, since widely adopted, marked the inauguration of the 'steam outline' miniature locomotive. It was built using as many standard Bassett Lowke 'Little Giant'-type parts as possible, so gaining some standardised components to bring it to some extent into line with the Atlantic-type steamer of Northampton manufacture.

This locomotive, named *Blacolvesley*, was a 15in gauge 4–4–4T and was commissioned by Mr C. W. Bartholomew for use on his railway at Blakesley Hall, Northamptonshire. It had a German NAG four-cylinder engine of 12–14hp and drove via a Heywood & Bridges friction clutch to a Wicksteed four-speed gearbox. All gears were separately engaged, and there was a separate reverse gear of Greenly design. Drive was via a shaft to axle-mounted bevel gear, and both axles had coupling rods as in steam practice. Main dimensions of the locomotive were: length over buffers 11ft $0\frac{3}{4}$in, height 3ft $3\frac{1}{2}$in, width 2ft 1in, coupled wheelbase 2ft 2in, total wheelbase 8ft $10\frac{1}{2}$in, driving wheel diameter $17\frac{3}{4}$in. The performance of this locomotive appears to have been outstanding for its day and since it was used to haul the hall's supplies such as coal, it seems to have been more of an industrial locomotive than one used solely for pleasure purposes on passenger trains. It was capable of hauling $4\frac{1}{2}$ tons up a 1 in 30 incline and of speeds in excess of 30mph. After changing hands several times, it was eventually acquired, together with a miniature railway at Saltburn, by Saltburn Motor Services, by which time it was fitted with an Austin 7 engine. It saw little use latterly and was sold to Mr T. Tate of Gateshead who, appreciating its historic value, restored it and still runs it on his premises at Haswell Lodge, Haswell, near Gateshead. This locomotive is the oldest surviving working internal-combustion locomotive in the world, unless, of course, some of the early McEwan Pratt examples still survive in the Far East!

J. W. Brooke & Co Ltd, Adrian Ironworks, Lowestoft, were, at about this time, installing their own Brooke petrol engines in a variety of units ranging from boats, stationary plants, motorcars, and railway inspection cars and trolleys. A few light railway haulage units, more akin to tramway practice than locomotives, were built and, although their history is obscure, one 1909 example was supplied to the Argentine. It was set to work hauling two 24-seater carriages over a short branch line. Under test at Lowestoft, it hauled two wagons of stone (36 tons)

Fig 8 *The world's oldest working petrol locomotive, the Bassett Lowke Blakesley Hall Railway unit of 1909, seen at work at Haswell, Co Durham, in October 1971 (15in gauge)*

with ease. In design the chassis followed tramway practice, as did the body, which was open from waist level up but had an overall canopy roof. This two-axle unit had a Brooke 45hp four-cylinder engine. Final drive was via a bevel gearbox on one axle with a cardan shaft to a similar gearbox on the other axle. The makers are now Brooke Marine Ltd of Lowestoft.

Strakers & Squire Ltd, London, established road vehicle manufacturers, built only one locomotive. This 1910 product was of 5ft 3in gauge and was supplied to the Guinness Brewery in Dublin. It was virtually a flat-topped frame on two axles, with an engine and transmission mounted on it.

Throughout the period 1900–10, William Peter Durtnall had been engaged on considerable research into the application of the internal-combustion engine and its development with associated transmission systems. It seems that he first became interested in the internal-combustion engine as a serious factor in rail traction after experience as a steam engineer on the Heilmann steam-electric locomotives which were tried out extensively on the Western Railway of France from 1893. These locomotives used an orthodox locomotive-type boiler to supply steam to high-speed steam engines of the Willans type which drove electric generators; in turn, these supplied electricity to the traction motors. The idea was to improve the steam engine and gain the economy, availability and convenience of electric traction without actually having to spend vast sums of money on electrification and the fixed equipment it entailed. The locomotive worked well on the

electrical side but the steam side of the system fell far short of the economy desired, and it was obvious that only a change of prime mover would justify further development.

With this in mind Durtnall turned his thoughts to the internal-combustion engine used with electric transmission. Much of his early work on improving the internal-combustion engine to give greater economy and reliability was undertaken quietly, mainly on road vehicles. Buses using a petrol-electric transmission to which Durtnall had applied his ideas were soon running in London with success, and his work on the Arnold Bennet racing-car of 1902 is well known.

In his work on the internal-combustion engine Durtnall achieved greater economy of fuel consumption by working the engines at constant speeds by means of electrical transmission rather than mechanical transmission via a gearbox, and vehicle speeds were controlled electrically independent of the engine. The water jacket around the cylinders was arranged to keep the water as warm as possible, so retaining the cylinders' heat inside and ensuring more efficient explosion of the air-fuel mixture. In engines of his own design, low-pressure steam was used instead of water and was obtained by the cooling water being turned into steam by the heat of the working engine. Great importance was attached to the correct adjustment and careful timing of the ignition, and air admission was a problem to which Durtnall devoted much time. Numerous patents covering many aspects of internal-combustion systems, transmissions, etc, were taken out by Durtnall and his associates under the 'Paragon' name.

In his railway work, numerous proposals for locomotives were put forward and designs prepared incorporating not only engines of the Durtnall type, but also his own traction motors and generators. The Paragon system of gearless rail traction used lightweight internal-combustion engines and was in direct opposition to the prevailing thought which centred on heavy, bulky engines and electrical equipment, although it was generally agreed that electrical transmission seemed desirable for rail traction. The fact that the diesel engine was still not readily available to meet Durtnall's requirements was constantly in his thoughts and his proposed 'Paragon Super Diesel Oil Engine', incorporating his 'Paragon silent long expansion stroke', was, he thought, the answer to this; meanwhile petrol or oil engines, suitably modified to include some of the Paragon ideas, would be used until his own engines were available. Some designs produced at this period did include petrol, kerosene and diesel engines, some driving two generators.

The silent, long-expansion-type engine, so much advocated by Durtnall, was designed to work equally well at sea level and high altitudes without losing power, the idea being that more air was taken in as the air pressure dropped so that the volume of air admitted remained the same regardless of its pressure. In practice, it was found that manufacturing problems would offset any theoretical advantage to be gained. The traction motors were carried adjacent to the axles and were mounted by being sprung from the bogie frame, the weight being taken up by the main bogie springs. The axles ran through a hollow rotor shaft, sufficient clearance being allowed in all directions. The traction motor was to run at the same speed as the axle, the drive being obtained by means of a special spring-drive device. The motors were capable of developing up to 250hp each at 450rpm.

The association of Durtnall with Hawthorn Leslies of Newcastle upon Tyne appears to date from about 1910, when the first inquiries were being received for internal-combustion locomotives of various types and sizes. A number of designs were prepared, but for various practical reasons, such as difficulties in regard to the transmission of high powers, none of them was built.

Hawthorn Leslies were fully aware of the problems from the start and were soon able, through their association with Durtnall, to offer a wide range of locomotives fitted with electrical transmissions based on Durtnall's patents under the Paragon sys-tem. Obvious customers were railways operating over barren, waterless routes, where fuel availability and the quality of the water posed problems, and these were the first to show an interest in motive power other than steam. Electric traction was available, but the internal combustion-engined locomotive offered a solution to their problems without the costly fixed equipment of electrification.

One of the designs prepared at this early date, a locomotive for use on the 1,000 mile Trans-Australian railway, was to have been a large double-bogie unit with six axles. The propulsion system was, of course, of the Paragon thermo-electric type, using petrol engines and electrical transmission and delivering some 800hp from the 1,000hp installation.

Durtnall's ideas on electrical transmission were quite revolutionary for his day and his plan to use his developed Paragon super diesel engine and his Paragon ac/dc transmission would certainly have produced a most interesting locomotive. Another of his far-sighted proposals was a form of squirrel cage traction motor, upon which experimental work is being carried out today—some sixty years later.

The 1,000hp locomotive was to have been built by the end of 1915 and tested for some 500 miles in England prior to shipment to Australia. As it was, the outbreak of war in 1914 put an end to the project and it was not until after the war that one of the Paragon locomotives was built. Further proposals included one for an eight-axle locomotive of 2,000hp, and a post-1920 design which will be discussed later. Emphatic claims were made by Durtnall and his builders, Hawthorn Leslies, as to their ability to guarantee the performance of their locomotives, including tractive effort and fuel consumption at different speeds, and to meet all potential requirements of an interested railway. Their locomotives, they claimed, would be capable of undertaking any type of traffic, for any particular purpose with all trailing loads at any speed, and of climbing any gradient!

The Paragon electro-magnetic control system included quite sophisticated devices in relation to engine control and electrical energy conservation. Braking was to be effected by means of the electric traction motors which, at the same time, could be used to charge the batteries. Another interesting point made by Durtnall and his builders was that they could offer locomotives to operate on any type of fuel: petrol, kerosene, heavy oils, tar gas, town gas, suction gas, alcohol, etc to suit local availability of supplies. This was to be made possible by supplying suitable fuel-production plants along with

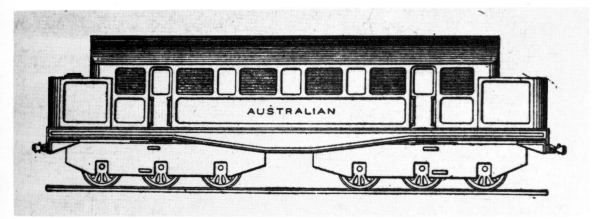

Fig 9 *The Trans–Australian 1,000hp Paragon thermo-electric to have been built by Hawthorn Leslie in 1914 but cancelled*

the locomotive and, in the case of suction gas, they hoped to incorporate a high-speed gas engine and a producer plant on the locomotive itself.

Durtnall went to great lengths to explain his ideas to practical engineers, the majority of whom did not understand or realise the importance of the system of traction he proposed, nor the advantages of locomotives with electric transmission. A certain stolidity of thought still clung to the reciprocating steam locomotive which had been built for over 100 years, with little improvement in efficiency apart from superheating (proposed, incidentally, during the 1830s by Hawthorns), and though the eventual eclipse of steam was foreseen by Durtnall, this was discounted by ardent steam locomotive engineers who failed to see the direction in which other coun-

tries' locomotive designers were heading. So it was that after World War II there came the closure of our oldest and largest locomotive builders, whose belated attempts to come to grips with modern traction failed to save them when steam orders vanished from their books almost overnight.

Charles Price & Sons Ltd of Broadheath, near Manchester, a firm manufacturing mainly agricultural equipment, were in the first decade of the twentieth century supplying small numbers of narrow-gauge locomotives, inspection trolleys of gauges up to 5ft 3in, and railcars, some of which were powered by petrol engines and transmissions of their own design. One model of 1911 was a two-axle 4½ ton locomotive of narrow-gauge type, powered by a 15–20hp petrol/paraffin engine. This unit

Fig 10 *Nasmyth Wilson's plantation locomotive for India in 1911 with body side panels removed (2ft 6in gauge)*

had a two-speed gearbox and was built with either jackshaft and side rod drive or axle drive.

Nearby at Bridgewater Foundry, Patricroft, Nasmyth Wilson & Co Ltd built their first petrol locomotive, an 0–4–0 type of 2ft 6in gauge for plantation work in India. Fitted with a Gardner four-cylinder engine developing 30hp at 750rpm, it had a friction clutch on the flywheel, a four-speed gearbox, a separate reverse gearbox, and cardan shaft drive to an axle-mounted worm-drive unit, both axles being coupled with side rods. In working order it weighed 7 tons and its overall dimensions were: length 15ft 7in; height 9ft 7½in; width 5ft 7in; wheelbase 6ft; wheel diameter 30in. Its top speed was 25mph and its maximum tractive effort 2,200lb. The overall roof was borne on four corner supports and carried the cooling water tank. Radiators were fitted at both ends.

The opening during 1911 of a small works at Lewes, in Sussex, by The Motor Rail & Tram Car Co Ltd marked the appearance on the scene of a firm which was later to have some impact on British locomotive design, especially in regard to contractors' types. Under the direction of Mr J. Dixon-Abbott they built mainly petrol tramcars and railcars at Lewes, apparently not as yet doing locomotive work.

Another important event of 1911 was the reappearance of Ernest E. Baguley on his return to Burton-upon-Trent to take over the Shobnall Road workshops of the Rykneild Motor Co Ltd from the liquidator. Having himself originally laid them out for Rykneilds, he knew they would meet the requirements of the business he was setting up to manufacture his own road vehicles. The firm, Baguley (Cars) Ltd, commenced production on road vehicles of various types, from motor lorries to private motor cars, usually incorporating the Baguley petrol engine and transmission system.

Production of the Drewry Car Co's railway vehicles began in 1912 and all types of railcars, inspection trolleys, and rolling stock were soon being built. The transfer of the Drewry work from the BSA works was a most fortuitous occurrence, as in addition to affording initial entry into the railway market of the Shobnall Road works, albeit as sub-contractors, it also provided a steady flow of work and scope for the use of Baguley engines and transmissions in this field. The influence of Baguley's work on British rail traction during the next fifteen years will be seen later.

A small incursion into the locomotive market at this period was that of Saunderson & Gifkins Ltd, Elstow Works, Bedford. In business for some time as agricultural engineers, they built a few paraffin-engined narrow-gauge rail tractors of low gear with an eye to selling them to the many local brickfields and quarries. These tractors had cylindrical water-cooling tanks mounted over the engines, three-speed gearboxes, cone clutches, and chain-axle drive with wheels coupled by side rods. The range comprised four types with either single- or twin-cylinder engines in the power range 6–16hp and weights of 1¼ tons–1 ton 17cwt. The speed range was 2, 4 and 8mph. The engine was mounted just off centre in front of the driver's position, the gearbox being located over the leading axle. Canopied cabs with large roofs reminiscent of traction engines were fitted as required. Very little is known of these machines or if many were sold. Within a few years the firm was trading as Saunderson & Mills Ltd and still offering its locomotives, a few of which are known to have been built after 1920.

After a lull of some six years, Kerr Stuart put in hand three very similar narrow-gauge petrol locomotives for experimental purposes. The first two, works Nos 1274/5, were ordered in April 1912 under order No 5813. The precise purpose of these locomotives is not entirely clear and confusion surrounds their building and subsequent fate. Both were similar in general design and appearance, akin to tramway locomotive design, and both were of 2ft 6in gauge and of 0–6–0 and 0–4–2 wheel arrangement respectively. It seems, though, that No 1274 may not actually have been completed, for though the engine, a Swedish Skindia two-cylinder marine oil engine of 45hp, was purchased for £397 7s 6d from Ekman & Co of Gothenburg, items were recorded as scrapped in July 1916, the engine was sold to T. W. Ward & Co Ltd in December 1917, and the clutch was later to be used on locomotive 1306.

Locomotive 1275, the 0–4–2 type unit, was built and tested. It had a Skindia two-cylinder marine oil engine of 30hp, costing £275 2s 0d, and outside frames which appear to have been rather similar to the Kerr Stuart narrow-gauge 0–4–2ST steam locomotive underframe. Final drive was by jackshaft and side rods.

The third locomotive, No 1306, may not have been built either but it was ordered in February 1913 for experimental purposes and was to have been fitted with a Gardner single-cylinder vertical engine and the Wrigglesworth clutch originally ordered for locomotive 1274. By mid-1915 the Gardner engine had been installed in the works' millwrights' shop and it is thought that the rest of the locomotive was scrapped. Wartime conditions were probably the reason for the discontinuance of these experiments.

An important occurrence in December 1912 was the failure of the old-established locomotive business of McEwan Pratt & Co Ltd. Fortunately, however, the McEwan Pratt name, so well known for quality if not business acumen, was not to fade from view, as the whole business, together with drawings, patents, etc, was subsequently taken over by Baguley (Cars) Ltd, Ernest Baguley seeing further scope for expansion of production at Shobnall Road. The old McEwan Pratt works at Wickford was closed down and sold and the manufacturing moved to Burton-upon-Trent where locomotive construction now started for the first time. Baguley (Cars) Ltd retained the well-established McEwan Pratt nameplate for its locomotives and, by arrangement, sales were handled by Mr Richard McEwan from his London office adjoining that of the Drewry Car Co Ltd.

The completion at Burton-upon-Trent during the 1913–14 period of two railcars, the first vehicles in the world successfully to employ hydraulic transmissions for rail use, aroused little interest. These were two petrol-hydraulic cars built by Baguley (Cars) Ltd for McEwan Pratt with Hele-Shaw hydrostatic transmissions. One was a large bogie car of 103hp for the Edmonton Inter-Urban Railway, Canada, and the other a two-axle 70hp car for Rhodesia. These vehicles are outside the scope of this work, but they are noteworthy as pre-dating German work of this type by many years.

Work was under way, as we shall see, with hydraulic transmission, and it is possible that the old Wickford works of McEwan Pratt may have designed and even built rail vehicles of this type at a still earlier date.

On the European continent development was hampered by problems of transmission, engine size and weight, and flexibility, although the work being carried on by MAN and Sulzer was to prove of value in the future. Typical of the transmission problems were the attempts at locomotives using forms of mechanical, direct drive, compressed air and electrical systems. In England, work on the latter system, which had seemed to hold promise, was stopped in 1914.

Eventually, it was the collaboration of Rudolph Diesel, Adolf Klose, Sulzer Bros, and Borsig, the German locomotive builders, which initiated the development of large locomotives using compression-ignition engines. In 1912 this consortium produced a 1,200hp mainline unit with a Sulzer-built diesel engine of the reversible type. Operating on the two-stroke principle, this engine had its four cylinders set in pairs in 'V' form at an angle of 90°. Drive was direct to a transversely mounted crankshaft across the centre of the locomotive between the two driving axles, which it drove by jackshaft and side rods. No intermediate transmission was used and the locomotive was set in motion and driven up to 6mph by means of compressed air in the diesel-engine cylinders, the air being supplied by an auxiliary compressor unit. Needless to say, the trials conducted on this 2–B–2 locomotive, both in Switzerland and in Germany, were failures because of its inflexibility and the difficulty of starting up the diesel side owing to the coolness of the cylinders after the use of compressed air, resulting in excessive fuel build-up and frequent misfires.

CHAPTER 4

1914-1919: A PERIOD OF GREAT ACTIVITY

THE years 1914-1919 gave a great fillip to the progress of the internal-combustion locomotive. In the United Kingdom, the war created a strong demand for such locomotives, and was met by manufacturers who in most instances had not previously carried out such work or, at best, in only a small way. The military demand for internal-combustion locomotives resulted in some very substantial orders and whilst, admittedly, these locomotives were generally of small size and low power the manufacturing experience gained was nonetheless valuable.

One newcomer to the field was W. G. Bagnall Ltd of Castle Engine Works, Stafford, who had been building steam locomotives since 1875. They built two small petrol locomotives in 1914, carrying works numbers in a new list prefixed by the letter 'P'. The first example, P50, was powered similarly to P51 but their appearance was totally different. Very little is known of the first locomotive but P51 was an 0–4–0 type locomotive built for use on a 1ft 11½in gauge railway in the Philippine Islands. The engine, possibly of Dorman manufacture, was a four-cylinder 40hp unit running at 1,200rpm. It had a two–speed gearbox giving 4 and 8mph. Final drive was by cardan shaft to a worm-drive unit on rear axle, both axles being rod-coupled. Weight in working order was 6 tons, overall length 16ft 10⅛in, height 8ft 4⅛in, width 5ft, wheelbase 4ft 10in, wheel diameter 19in.

Baguley (Cars) Ltd were also still building locomotives in accordance with the old Wickford works practice for, though re-design work was in progress following their purchase of the McEwan Pratt business, this had not yet been finalised. Sales during 1914 included four locomotives of the plantation type of McEwan Pratt to the Jokai tea gardens, carrying works Nos 534/5/67 and 809.

A similar 0–4–0 chain-driven centre-cab locomotive was sold in October 1914 for service on the 18in gauge Woolwich Arsenal Railway. This 'type J' locomotive was possibly originally built at Wickford, but was unsold at the time of closure. It was brought to Burton-upon-Trent, regauged, given works No 630 and sold to meet this order. This unit, named *Megaera*, is well known and was, it seems, the only pure McEwan Pratt-built locomotive to work in the United Kingdom.

In addition to putting a stop to the 'Paragon' locomotive, the war also ended the ambitious project commenced at Burton-upon-Trent—the world's first locomotive with hydraulic transmission. This was the 0–4–0 petrol-hydraulic by Baguley (Cars) Ltd for McEwan Pratt & Co Ltd, intended for the Lachine Railway, Canada. This standard-gauge unit was to have been powered by a White & Poppe 150hp six-cylinder engine and to employ a Hele-Shaw hydrostatic transmission. Work ceased on this locomotive after completion of the underframe and testing of the transmission at the Baguley works. Allocated works No 621, the locomotive's main dimensions would have been: length over head-stocks 21ft, height 11ft, wheelbase 7ft, wheel diameter 41in. The tractive effort at 3·75mph has been assessed at about 15,000lb. The underframe and wheels were used in 1921 to build the only stand-ard-gauge steam locomotive ever produced by Baguleys and sold for service as a shunter to a local brewery.

The absence up to this time of the so-called traditional locomotive builders—apart from Bagnalls and Kerr Stuarts—from the internal-combustion locomotive market was now about to be rectified, at least by the smaller locomotive builders. This is not to say that much thinking and design work in this field had not previously taken place, and in the case of the Avonside Engine Co Ltd of Bristol, long established as industrial steam locomotive specialists, although originally also builders of mainline locomotives, a number of proposals going back to the 1910–12 period have come to light. Their first internal-combustion locomotives were

Fig 11 Maria, *W. G. Bagnall's second petrol locomotive, a 1ft 11½in gauge machine of 1914 for the Philippines*

built in 1914 and were small 0–4–0 petrol units about which little is known, although they were apparently of very similar design.

The first, carrying works No 1688, was named *Nyali No 2*, but to whom it was delivered is not known, although drawings of the type were supplied to Robert Hudson Ltd, the light railway engineers at Leeds, who illustrated this locomotive in their contemporary catalogues, and also to the War Office in 1914. The locomotive was 10ft 1¼in in overall length, height 9ft 3in, width 5ft 8in, wheelbase 3ft, wheel diameter 21in; final drive was by jackshaft and side rods.

Avonside 1689 was an 18in-gauge unit powered by a four-cylinder petrol-paraffin engine of 25–8hp and driving via a two-speed gearbox and jackshaft to the wheels by side rods. Overall length was 10ft 1¼in, height 8ft 6in, width 4ft 10½in, wheelbase 3ft. Locomotives 1699/1700 had similar engines and transmissions and dimensions were identical except that their height was 9ft 3in. At 3mph the tractive effort was quoted at 1,900lb. All were definitely narrow gauge and appear to have been exported.

The year 1915 marked the entry of The Motor Rail & Tram Car Co Ltd into the locomotive business, operating now from a works purchased in Elstow Road, Bedford, and still under the direction of Mr J. Dixon-Abbott. The basic excellence

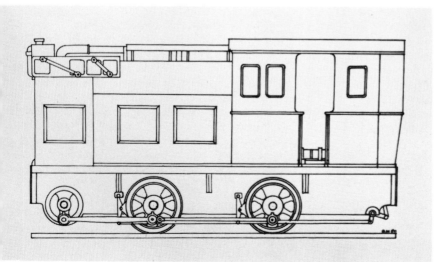

Fig 12 *The world's first locomotive with hydraulic transmission. The never-completed Baguley–McEwan Pratt 150hp 0–4–0PH for Canada,* BG 621

Fig 13 *One of the ex-*WDLR *20hp 2½-ton Simplex units at York Corporation sewage works in 1970,* MR *1111 of 2ft gauge. This unit has now been preserved*

and robustness of the simple locomotive they produced, so aptly named the 'Simplex', has been proved by its steady development since 1915 while still retaining the transverse engine layout; it is still in production today.

The use of the transverse engine mounting, echoing that of Britain's first oil-engined locomotive by Priestman, simplified the transmission by cutting out costly bevel gears to convert the engine output by a right-angled axle drive as found in locomotives, with lengthways or longitudinally mounted engines. As the engine and gearbox output was at the same plane as the locomotive wheels, it was a simple matter to drive the axles by roller chains. The idea was later copied by other locomotive builders, notably Planet, Hunslet, Hudswell Clarke, Fowler, Drewry and Baguley.

The first Simplex design was a bow-framed 2½ ton, 20hp, two-axle locomotive built in very large numbers for war service on 60cm gauge lines. Production of these built up from early 1916, following proving trials both in the United Kingdom and at the testing centre at Audricq in France, where extensive trials of all WDLR petrol locomotive designs were undertaken by the Railway Operating Division of the Royal Engineers. The engine was a two-cylinder 20hp petrol type built by Dormans at Stafford to Mr Dixon-Abbott's requirements. The transmission was an inverted cone clutch with shaft drive to a Dixon-Abbott patent two-speed David Brown-built gearbox with roller chains driving to both axles. Overall dimensions were: length 9ft, height 4ft 6in (no cab being fitted), width 5ft, wheelbase 3ft 6in, wheel diameter 17¾in; the speeds were 3·4 and 8·2mph.

The mechanical design of the Simplex included a massive underframe built up from rolled-steel sections secured by rivetting and bolts. This open structure took the running and buffing gear, the engine and transmission being placed on top of this to give excellent accessibility. Motor Rail's practice of purchasing components from outside suppliers who built to Simplex designs greatly enhanced the efficiency of the works, enabling it to operate with a small staff who erected the locomotives from the parts and ensuring a much higher production rate than would otherwise have been possible.

The 2½ ton design was closely followed by a special design, also of 60cm gauge, weighing 6 tons. This was available in two basic forms, both of which had armour-plating for use in forward

Fig 14 *One of the 6-ton 40hp Simplex locomotives of the* WDLR *built in 1918 and still in service with Leeds Corporation at Knostropp sewage works. This example is of the protected type (2ft gauge)*

areas of the European battlefield—the armoured type, fitted with bullet-proof front and rear, roof, sliding side doors, and slit-type cab side and front windows; the protected type, which was very similar but only had bullet-proof front and rear and roof, the sides being fitted with sliding doors, and open front and rear windows. A simplified version of the latter model, without the sliding side doors, was also produced, side protection for the crew being provided only by roll-down canvas weathersheets. Transfer of components from locomotive to locomotive resulted in some 'hybrid' units, and it was even possible to find an armoured version

running with canvas side sheets, etc. These locomotives had the same type of Dorman engine but with four cylinders and 40hp rating. The transmission was similar, too, as was the speed range. Overall dimensions were: length 11ft 0½in, height 8ft 4in, width 6ft 8in, wheelbase 4ft, wheel diameter 18in. There is little doubt that the Simplex locomotives, with their rugged construction and proven reliability, were the backbone of the WDLR light railway networks. In all, Motor Rail & Tramcar Co Ltd supplied some 1,000–1,100 petrol locomotives for war service.

A standard-gauge protected type, weighing 8

Fig 15 *A Simplex armoured standard-gauge 8-ton 40hp unit for the* ROD *during World War I*

Fig 16 *The Avonside Engine Co supplied twelve of these petrol units to the War Office in 1915,* AE *1703–14 (2ft 6in gauge)*

tons, was also produced with engine and transmission similar to the 40hp 60cm-gauge type. Overall dimensions were: length 13ft 4in, height 9ft 7in, width 6ft 9½in, wheelbase 5ft 6in, wheel diameter 37in; speeds were 3 and 7·2mph.

In all cases it is apparent that extensive standardisation was achieved and the same three types were made available commercially, without, of course, armour-plating, after military requirements had ceased.

Another design prompted by a War Office inquiry resulted in an order for a batch of twelve locomotives of 2ft 6in gauge, placed with the Avonside Engine Co Ltd, Bristol. Carrying works Nos 1703–14, they were delivered during 1915, numbered 31–42 in the War Office series. It is not certain where these locomotives were set to work, but it may have been in Egypt, where similar locomotives of Hawthorn Leslie build had been sent. These 'Avonsides' had Parsons vertical four-cylinder engines of 60hp at 550rpm, and a normal clutch and gearbox gave them speeds of 2½, 5, 10 and 15 mph. Weight in working order was 9 tons 2cwt, overall dimensions being length 12ft 1½in, height 8ft 9in, width 5ft 6in, wheelbase 4ft, wheel diameter 24in; maximum tractive effort was 5,800lb.

Though actively engaged for some time in design work in the internal-combustion locomotive field, R. & W. Hawthorn Leslie & Co had not actually built any until their first production order in 1915. This was a small straightforward 0–4–0 petrol machine of 2ft 6in gauge built to War Office requirements. The order was for twenty-three loco-

motives for use on the line constructed and operated by the Royal Engineers between Port Said and Qalaat in Egypt. They carried works Nos 3107–29 and were numbered 61–83 on the cab side to meet War Office requirements, with small plates inside the cabs, 'R.O.D. Egypt B747–69'. They had Gardner four-cylinder marine-type engines of 55hp at 600rpm. The transmission included a disc-type friction clutch and three-speed gearbox, giving speeds of 4, 8 and 15mph. Coupling rods connected the axles which were worm-driven from the gearbox. Weight in working order was 8¾ tons, their wheelbase being 5ft and wheel diameter 27in.

Baguley (Cars) Ltd built in February 1915 for McEwan Pratt a 45cm 0–4–0 petrol/paraffin locomotive of special design, in that it was a transitional design incorporating some of the forthcoming new Baguley–McEwan Pratt ideas and those of the Wickford works ideas which were still relevant. The power-equipment layout followed Wickford practice, as did the provision of external railcar-type horizontal radiators at each end of the locomotive, but the use of the jackshaft and side rod drive was akin to the new McEwan Pratt range of locomotives then being evolved at Burton-upon-Trent; as yet the large cylindrical water-cooling tank was not used. Carrying works No 625, it was a mining locomotive built to the order of Matheson & Co Ltd and supplied for use overseas. A 10hp two-cylinder Baguley engine was fitted with a transmission of the McEwan Pratt type with a plate-type clutch and two-speed gearbox giving speeds of 4·5 and 9 mph. Weight in working order was 11 tons 17cwt and its dimensions were: length 9ft, height over cab roof 4ft 11in, width 2ft 3½in, wheelbase 3ft, wheel diameter 18in. An overall canopy roof was fitted, supported at each corner; water tanks were located at each end with a centre fuel tank. The exhaust was carried underneath before release and the driver sat with his legs on either side of the engine.

The new McEwan Pratt company was registered on 20 April 1915 as a subsidiary of Baguley (Cars) Ltd, sales continuing to be conducted from the London office under the guidance of Mr Richard McEwan.

The new range of McEwan Pratt locomotives was now being finalised and the chief draughtsman at Baguley (Cars) Ltd, Leonard Benthall, deserves special mention for his work in developing the excellent 'new' McEwan Pratt locomotive range which totally replaced the somewhat outdated Wickford designs. At this period the Baguley works in Shobnall Road was engaged in building petrol engines, transmissions and locomotives for McEwan Pratt, and railcars and inspection trolleys for the Drewry Car Co. Railway rolling stock, motor road vehicles, and general engineering work was also being undertaken.

To meet further government demands for locomotives suitable for use in munitions and gun-powder factories, Ruston & Proctor Ltd of Lincoln, who had built a few steam locomotives for various customers in the period 1860–90, produced a paraffin locomotive. Similar in both layout and external appearance to the German Deutz locomotive, it incorporated the Ruston-type ZRH horizontal engine. About a dozen of these locomotives were supplied between June 1915 and March 1918 with the 10hp Ruston engine. The ZRH engine, a single-cylinder type, was started by petrol, having a magneto for the ignition, and once underway, ran on paraffin. The engine drove a crankshaft with a heavy flywheel at each end, situated midway along each side of the locomotive above and between the two axles. For stationary applications this type of engine had a governor on the camshaft, arranged to allow the exhaust valve to slip when normal speed was exceeded, so preventing the exhaust valve from opening. By this arrangement the inlet valve did not open, as the inlet valve lever only operated the inlet-valve spring on the next stroke, the heat being retained in the cylinder when an explosion was missed. It seems that this ingenious idea was replaced on the locomotive engines by a gear-driven governor. The clutch was a Johnstone coil type, the clutches being engaged by a cab hand-wheel turning either clockwise or anti-clockwise. The two-speed gearbox, forward and reverse, drove to the

Fig 17 *A Ruston & Proctor 'reproduction' of a German Deutz design for use in ordnance and munitions works during World War I. This is a 10hp narrow-gauge unit at work at Holton Heath*

rear axle by chains, both axles being coupled by a further chain. The heavy flywheels provided the initial inertia for these low-powered locomotives to start heavy trains.

Deliveries of these locomotives included some to factories at London, Faversham, Holton Heath, Enfield Lock, and also to the Admiralty, and at many factories they had women drivers.

Gauges varied between 1ft 6in and 2ft 6in and both inside- and outside-framed types were supplied. Weight in working order was 4 tons: length over buffers was 11ft 6in, height 6ft, width 3ft 6in and maximum tractive effort at low speed, 3mph, was 800lb. The engines exhausted up the chimney. The first locomotive of this type was subsequently rescued from a quarry on the edge of Dartmoor by an enthusiast who has preserved it. This locomotive carried works No 50823.

Concurrently with the 10hp design, a locomotive with a two-cylinder horizontal engine, type 20HD, was built; it weighed 6 tons and was very similar to the 10hp type. Two were supplied in September/October 1915 to Buxton Lime Firms Ltd (RP 50896, RP 51615) and, although of uncertain rail gauge, may have worked at Peak Forest, Derbyshire. These locomotives were of 20hp and were 12ft in length, height 6ft, width 4ft 3in, with a tractive effort at 3mph of 1,600lb.

The Leeds firm of Manning Wardle & Co Ltd received their first internal-combustion locomotive order in November 1914 and commenced delivery a year later, in October 1915. The order came from the War Office and was for ten large 0–4–0 petrol locomotives of standard gauge with armour-plated superstructures for heavy haulage of rail-mounted guns. These machines (MW 1867–76) were fitted with a John I. Thornycroft six–cylinder marine engine, type S6 of 180hp at 550rpm. The transmission was a Thornycroft-type 6H friction clutch bolted to a heavy flywheel, Kayser Ellison gears and universal coupling, giving speeds of 5, 13 and 26 mph. Final drive was by cardan shaft to worm-drive unit at one end of one axle, and both axles were coupled by side rods. The locomotives carried Nos 1–10 painted on the cab sides. Deliveries were as follows: No 1 to Longmoor (27 October 1915); Nos 2–4 to Egypt (25 January 1916); Nos 5–7 to France (10 April 1916); and Nos 8–10 to France (26 April 1916 and 1 May 1916). The locomotives proved wholly unsuccessful and after frequent breakdowns were soon relegated to shunting work.

The introduction during 1916 of the Baguley-built, newly designed McEwan Pratt locomotive range was a great step forward in the development of the British internal-combustion industrial locomotive. Baguley's locomotive work was, without doubt, far in advance of any other British locomotive builder's work at that time, both in robustness of construction and good design. Baguley locomotives were not mass produced and were not cheap, so production was limited. They were designed to compete with steam traction rather than be a cheap substitute for it, and it was less expensive to purchase an equivalent steam locomotive than a Baguley–McEwan Pratt petrol locomotive. They were designed by Ernest Baguley and Leonard Benthall to cover the 10–150hp range using, where possible, Baguley petrol engines and Baguley transmissions, all manufactured at Shobnall Road works.

In February 1916 two Baguley 10hp 0–4–0 locomotives were delivered to the War Office for evaluation. These locomotives, works Nos 677/8, were ordered through Rendell, Palmer & Tritton and after successful trials in England a large order was placed by the War Office.

The two prototypes had Baguley two-cylinder 10hp engines running at 1,000rpm, driving via a cone clutch, bevel gears, two-speed gearbox, giving 3·75 and 7·5mph, with jackshaft and side rod drive. Overall dimensions were: length 9ft $0\frac{1}{4}$in, height over cab 8ft $3\frac{3}{4}$in, width 3ft 6in, wheelbase 3ft, wheel diameter 18in; the maximum tractive effort was 800lb and weight in working order 1 ton $17\frac{3}{4}$ cwt.

The production locomotives were the same except that the wheelbase was 2ft 6in, and over seventy locomotives were built, being supplied mainly to the WDLR, the War Office, Air Ministry and RAF. Some fifteen examples also went to the Board of Trade timber camps, and Inland Waterways and Docks boards. There were slight variations as different batches were built but basically they were standardised in regard to power and transmission equipment; the majority were delivered without cabs, having open footplates.

The locomotives sent to Europe were set to work on lightly and roughly laid railway networks where, not surprisingly, they did not prove anything like as successful as the prototypes which had been tested over well-laid rails in England. They were underpowered for the loads they were required to haul over rough trackwork and though the absence of smoke or steam made them less conspicuous to the enemy when working within artillery range, the exhaust pipe of the 10hp McEwan Pratt was apt to glow red hot in the dark and so make night driving a somewhat hazardous occupation. Upon relegation to lighter duties they proved more successful, and

Fig 18 *16hp and 60hp Baguley–McEwan Pratt loco-motives outside Shobnall Road works in 1918,* BG *685 and 702 respectively; the latter went to the Associated Equipment Co Ltd, London. The 10hp* WDLR *units were similar to 685*

after the war many of them found their way into narrow-gauge industrial service, both in Europe and England. Fortunately, three of this general type, two of which are in almost original condition, have been preserved by enthusiasts.

The first internal-combustion locomotive to be built by the Scottish locomotive builders, Andrew Barclay, Sons & Co Ltd of Caledonia Works, Kilmarnock, appeared during 1916. This obscure 3ft gauge unit was a two-axle design fitted with a single-cylinder petrol engine of 10–12hp and was built for use at the Bradford Road Gasworks at Manchester.

Still producing a few railway internal-combustion vehicles from their Broadheath works were Charles Price & Sons Ltd, examples of designs of this period being a 4½ ton and a 5½ ton type in the 20–30hp range, powered by Price petrol engines, clutches and epicyclic gearboxes. They were built to the designs of T. A. Borthwick and F. C. Price.

Some of the largest of the Baguley (Cars) Ltd petrol locomotives were three McEwan Pratt standard-gauge 0–4–0 units built during the period 1915–18. During 1915 the agents, A. G. Evans & Co, who sold many Baguley-built products for McEwan Pratt and Drewry Car Co, placed an order for a locomotive for London & Thames Haven Oil Wharves Ltd. This locomotive (BG 566) was a 60hp type, powered by a four-cylinder White & Poppe vertical petrol engine running at 900rpm, and was delivered in July 1916. The transmission was of the Baguley patent type and incorporated a cone-type clutch and a two-speed gearbox giving speeds of 3½ and 6mph with final drive by spur drive to a jack-shaft unit and side rods. At 3½mph the tractive effort was 4,875lb. The overall dimensions were: length 17ft 2½in, height 9ft 7½in, width 7ft, wheelbase 5ft 6in, wheel diameter 30in; weight in working order was 6 tons 14cwt.

The two further examples were generally similar

Fig 19 *The Beamish Museum preserved 60hp Baguley–McEwan Pratt machine seen here in February 1968 at Jacob's Biscuit Works, Aintree,* BG *680/16*

to 566. The first, No 680, was delivered in August 1916 to Richard Johnson & Nephew Ltd, Aintree, for use at their munitions works. This locomotive remained at Aintree, and in 1919 it was taken over by W. & R. Jacob & Co Ltd, biscuit makers, for use at their factory. A new engine replacing the White & Poppe was installed in 1927, this being a Baguley four-cylinder petrol engine of 60hp. In February 1968, after overhaul and repainting, it was presented to Bowes Museum for eventual display in working order at the industrial open-air museum which is being set up under their auspices at Beamish, County Durham.

The third locomotive, No 702, was delivered to the Associated Equipment Co Ltd (AEC) in April 1918 for use at their Walthamstow lorry and bus factory. This locomotive differed slightly in being fractionally longer and higher with wheels of 42in diameter, but was otherwise identical.

Perhaps one of the most interesting of the petrol locomotive designs built for the WDLR was the 60cm-gauge petrol-electric two-axle unit, supplied by Dick Kerr & Co and British Westinghouse. This order, for 200 locomotives of basically similar design, was placed by the Railway Operating Division of the Royal Engineers in November 1916 and divided equally between the two manufacturers.

The Dick Kerr locomotives, to be numbered LR 2001–2100 by the WDLR, were built at Preston and had a Dorman-type 4JO four-cylinder petrol engine of 40hp which drove a Phoenix (Bradford) generator, supplying power to two nose-suspended axle-hung traction motors with single-reduction gear drive, of Dick Kerr manufacture. They weighed 8 tons in working order and their overall dimensions were: length 15ft 1in, height 8ft 8in, width 5ft 6in, wheelbase 5ft 6in, wheel diameter 32in, while their top speed was 20mph.

The British Westinghouse locomotives were subcontracted for mechanical parts to Nasmyth Wilson & Co Ltd, and these locomotives should have carried Nos 1901–2000 in the WDLR series and were Nasmyth Wilson works Nos 1144–1243. Of these locomotives, ninety-four had the Dorman 4JO engine set at 38hp, while the remaining six had Tylor 45hp engines. The electrical equipment, generator and traction motors were supplied by British Westinghouse Ltd (Metropolitan Vickers Ltd). Mechanical details were identical to the Dick Kerr examples but superficial differences, such as placing of louvres and bonnet side access door design, were apparent. Dimensions, too, were the same but they were lighter in weight at 7·5 tons. All the mechanical portions were subcontracted and built at Leeds by the Leeds Forge Co Ltd, well-known railway rolling stock makers, but final erection and installation of power equipment was carried out mainly at West's Gas Appliance Works at Miles Platting, Manchester, who completed ninety-seven locomotives, as Nasmyth Wilson's Patricroft works were then fully engaged on other wartime activities.

For some reason the number series allocated by WDLR became transposed when delivery started, so that the British Westinghouse batch took the numbers 2001–2100, originally allotted to the Dick Kerr units, and vice versa. It is suggested, and affirmed by English Electric, Dick Kerr's successors, that the locomotives were capable of conversion to operate from overhead electric catenary, so enabling the petrol prime mover and its generator to be shut down and the traction motors operated like a straight electric locomotive. Illustrations of both batches of locomotives reveal fittings on their bonnet tops evidently designed to take the current collection equipment for this.

Testing was carried out at Dinas Junction on the Welsh Highland Railway, and at Longmoor, of a small batch of the first completed by Dick Kerr, but it seems that all the remainder and the Westinghouse batch were sent straight to Europe.

Both designs had armoured cabs and were designed to operate in pairs, cab to cab. A few of these locomotives survive today on the Continent and at least one has been shipped back to England from France for preservation. Others were rebuilt for use in England on standard-gauge lines by railway demolition contractors, and the Ashover Light Railway in Derbyshire had one named *Amos* for many years. Although troublesome machines in operation, not to mention their noise when at work, their basic concept with axle-hung motors was a pointer to future developments and as such the design may be considered as the ancestor of the ubiquitous British Railways diesel electric shunter of today. In 1918 Dick Kerr, together with Willans at Rugby, Siemens Bros at Stafford, and Phoenix at Bradford, amalgamated to form the English Electric Co Ltd.

Further machines for use in government factories were built at Burton upon Trent by Baguley (Cars) Ltd during the second half of 1917. The first of these were some simple rail tractors incorporating many parts used in the manufacture of Drewry railcars and inspection trolleys and, for this reason, sold under the Drewry Car Co Ltd nameplate, the first locomotives to be so sold. They were fitted with the same engine as used in Drewry Car products, namely the Baguley 'R' type—a

Fig 20 *The mechanical portion of a British Westinghouse World War 1 4WPE built by Leeds Forge Ltd for Nasmyth Wilson (60cm gauge)*

Fig 21 *A Dick Kerr-built 4WPE on test on the Welsh Highland Railway in February 1917. In* WDLR *service they operated in pairs cab to cab (60cm gauge)*

Fig 22 *The Baguley-built Drewry rail tractors—this example was for the Ministry of Munitions at Aintree (2ft gauge)*

Fig 23 *The sophisticated Baguley–McEwan Pratt 60hp 0–6–0*PM *units for the French War Office in 1917–18,* BG *686–95 (60cm gauge)*

single-cylinder 6hp vertical unit driving into a simple railcar-type gearbox with chain drive to the axles. Overall dimensions of these tractors were: length over buffer beams 5ft 11½in, height (they had no cab) 4ft 6in, width 3ft 0½in, wheelbase 2ft 6in, wheel diameter 19in, rail gauge 2ft. Under the original order, nine were built between July 1917 and October 1918, carrying Baguley works Nos 699–701, 846–10 and 997. Seven were sent to the National Filling Factory No 2 at Aintree, and two, 700/1, to the No 7 factory at Northolt. Only a few further examples were ever built and it is surprising, considering the simplicity of their design and the later popularity of other makes of light rail tractors, that they were not produced in much greater numbers.

In complete contrast to the light rail tractors, the same builder turned out during September 1917 one of the most advanced and certainly the most sophisticated narrow-gauge petrol locomotive type ever produced. This interesting design was to an order from the French government obtained for Baguley (Cars) Ltd by McEwan Pratt & Co Ltd after failure to find a continental locomotive builder prepared to meet the exacting demands of the specification. The original specification was for a 150hp locomotive but designs submitted by McEwan Pratt–Baguley included a 100hp 0–4–0+0–4–0, and a 60hp 0–6–0. Requirements were that a load of 177 tons be hauled at 3·12mph on the level, and that gradients of 1 in 15 maximum and curves of 20m be negotiated.

The 60hp 0–6–0 design was eventually chosen by the French War Office, to be built to a rail gauge of 60cm. The locomotives carried works Nos 686–95 in the Baguley list and bore cast number plates on the cab sides numbered 1001–10. These very substantial units had armour-plating and were fitted with the following equipment: a power-driven winch with 150m of wire rope; a powered capstan; water pump of 900gal/min capacity; tool boxes which were capable of being used to carry ballast to increase adhesion; and re–railing jacks.

Instrumentation, in addition to normal locomotive controls, included fuel gauges, oil pressure gauges, speedometer, mileage recorder, inclinometer, spring-deflection gauges and a drawbar pull dynamometer; all were fluorescent and shielded so as not to be visible outside, and electric lighting was fitted. The engine was a White & Poppe four-cylinder unit developing 60hp at 900rpm. The transmission included a cone-type clutch, a two-speed gearbox giving 3·12 and 12·5mph; final drive was by jackshaft and side rods under the cab. The manufacture of the underframes, flycranks and side rod drive was undertaken at Stoke-on-Trent by Kerr Stuart & Co, who gave them works Nos 3052–61 in their lists.

Design, construction and testing were all under surveillance of a French army officer who saw to it that the specification, even down to the number plates, was fully adhered to. Testing was carried out at Shobnall Road works on a special test track

Fig 24 *One of the twenty 180hp 0-4-0*PM *locomotives by Manning Wardle in the 1915–18 period. Built to the order of the War Office and Ministry of Munitions*

with figure eight curves of down to 20m radius and a gradient of 1 in 20. The tests being completed successfully, delivery commenced and was completed in July 1918. Overall dimensions were: length over buffers 13ft 11¼in, height 6ft 6in, width 5ft 6½in, wheelbase 5ft 4in, wheel diameter 26½in; weight in working order was 7 tons 11cwt.

Manning Wardle built a further ten of the standard-gauge 0-4-0 petrol locomotives, generally similar in design to the 1915–16 batch, and delivered them between February and June 1918. Carrying works Nos 1945–54, they were ordered in February 1917 by the Ministry of Munitions, Railway Materials Branch, and, in view of the poor performance of the previous batch, were not put to work on duties demanding high availability. They were numbered 1691–700 on cast-iron cab side plates and were put to work as depot shunters, the first six going to the Ministry of Munitions at Sandwich, while others went to Griffiths Wharf, Woolwich, London, and various other depots.

The design was very like that of the first batch and some saw further use in industrial applications after the war, although their generally poor standard of reliability gave them a short life. One example, No 1700, lasted until well after World War II, albeit after removal of its 'innards' and replacement by a vertical boiler and engine of steam type by Sentinels at Roads Reconstruction Ltd, Cranmore Depot.

Fig 25 *One of six 20hp 0-4-*PM *units by Baguley–McEwan Pratt for use on government timber camp railways in 1919 of which one has been preserved,* BG *774–9 (1ft 11½in gauge)*

During September 1918 the firms of Ruston & Proctor Ltd and Richard Hornsby & Sons Ltd joined forces to form Ruston & Hornsby Ltd with factories at Grantham and Lincoln. Very little was done with locomotives apart from three 6 ton twin-cylinder machines for the Barsi Light Railway in India. These were two-axle shunters rather similar to the 1915 munitions factory locomotives built by Ruston & Proctor; they were delivered in 1920. Ruston & Hornsby were to become established in locomotive work after 1930.

Between February and April 1919 Baguley (Cars) Ltd supplied six 2ft-gauge petrol locomotives to the Board of Trade for use on timber camp railways operated by the Timber Supply Department in various parts of the country. This standard McEwan Pratt design was an 0–4–0 type unit fitted with a Baguley four-cylinder engine of 20hp. This drove via a Baguley transmission, incorporating a cone clutch of the compound type, a constant mesh gearbox which drove to a transverse shaft and Baguley jackshaft final drive unit mounted at the front end of the locomotive. The front final drive

arrangement was new to Baguley-McEwan Pratt practice, the majority of locomotives having previously employed a rear-mounted final drive. These were the first locomotives by Baguleys, and one of the first ever, to have a gearchange not incorporating sliding dogs.

Weighing 6½ tons, their overall dimensions were: length 10ft 8in, height 5ft 9in, width 4ft, wheelbase 2ft 9in, wheel diameter 20½in, speeds being 3 and 6mph. They carried works Nos 774–9 and some were apparently re-purchased by Baguleys, since one example, locomotive No 774, was re-painted, suitably disguised with metal plating to cover the transmission, and exhibited as a current production at the British Empire Exhibition, Wembley, in 1924. In 1927 it was sold to the Oakley Slate Quarries of Blaenau Festiniog, North Wales, where, after being laid aside, it became walled inside a workshop. There No 774 remained for many years until 1966 when it was found, in excellent condition and still in its Wembley paintwork, and was purchased by an enthusiast for preservation.

CHAPTER 5

1920-1925: MORE INDUSTRIAL AND EXPERIMENTAL LOCOMOTIVES

THOUGH the war period had stimulated the production of smaller internal-combustion locomotives it had also put a stop to a number of developments in the British locomotive industry which might have had far-reaching effects, in that they concerned large mainline proposals.

Hawthorn Leslie & Co produced a number of diesel locomotive proposals independent of W. P. Durtnall's ideas, some of which were very interesting. One of these was an amazing standard-gauge diesel mechanical locomotive for freight haulage on an 'important railway'. It was to have been powered by an air-started Atlas diesel engine of vertical six-cylinder type, rated to give 800hp at 420rpm. The transmission was to have been a massive Wilson unit incorporating epicyclic gears, brought into action by braking the respective drums in which the gears were arranged; jackshaft and side rod drive was proposed. Weight in working order was estimated at 81 tons, of which 64 tons

were available for adhesion. Overall dimensions were: length 43ft 8in, height 13ft 5in, width 9ft, rigid wheelbase 15ft, total wheelbase 35ft, driving wheel diameter $52\frac{1}{2}$in. The wheel notation was 1–D–1 and top speed was up to 26mph, with a maximum starting tractive effort of 35,840lb. Imagine the sight of a pair of these climbing up to Consett Ironworks with an iron ore train, or 'belting' along the straight between York and Darlington!

Another design bearing definite Hawthorn Leslie characteristics which turned up among BR material at York was an outline proposal for a large express passenger locomotive, supposedly for the North Eastern Railway. This 105 ton machine with a 21 ton axle loading was to have been 49ft in overall length, 13ft 1in in height, have a rigid coupled wheelbase of 15ft, total wheelbase of 40ft 6in and driving wheels of 6ft $8\frac{1}{2}$in in diameter. The wheel arrangement was 2–C–2 and its engine appears to

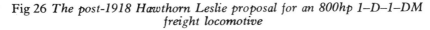

Fig 26 *The post-1918 Hawthorn Leslie proposal for an 800hp 1–D–1–DM freight locomotive*

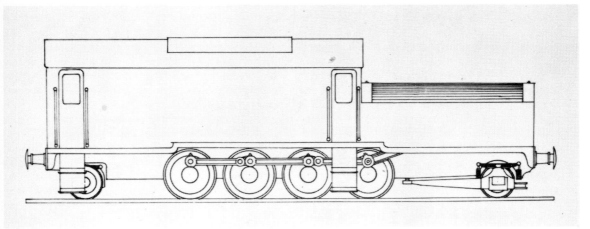

Fig 27 *The sole Durtnall Paragon thermo-electric locomotive ever built. A Hawthorn Leslie experimental 320hp design of 1920,* HL *3500/20*

have followed marine practice, but its type or make had not been defined, neither has its transmission type, which was to have been mechanical and driving via jackshaft and side rods to the three coupled axles. The close proximity of the rod drive to the bogie would have seriously restricted its operation except round maximum radius curves.

Another Hawthorn Leslie design was for an 0–6–0DH with Lentz transmission and an Atlas six-cylinder 400hp engine running at 475rpm. This diesel hydraulic shunter would have weighed 48·25 tons.

William Beardmore & Co Ltd, Dalmuir Works, Glasgow, did a certain amount of work on diesel traction and one of their designs was for a large plate-framed 1–E–1 machine of 600hp, with mechanical jackshaft and side rod transmission. This company's main work in this field was to come with the introduction of the Beardmore diesel engine range, rather than with actual diesel locomotives.

At long last Hawthorn Leslies put in hand a 'Paragon' locomotive to Capt W. P. Durtnall's designs. This petrol-electric, or thermo-electric, locomotive was a double bogie machine built purely for experimental purposes. Carrying works No 3500, it had a full-width, full-length cab superstructure and two second-hand petrol engines modified to conform in some respects to Durtnall's ideas on engine design, which were taken from coastal motor boats. The engines were of the six-cylinder in-line type, developing 160hp and 450 rpm, and were mounted at each end of a 6 pole DC generator with poles of 220kW capacity at 440V,

placed in the centre of the locomotive. The traction motors were four of 68hp running at 1,200rpm fixed longitudinally at each end of each bogie. They drove via flexible couplings and cardan shaft to worm gearing mounted on the axles of the remote pair of driving wheels with a ratio of 733 : 1.

The air compressor for the brakes, and a small DC generator for battery charging for excitation of the main generator and main engine starting, lighting etc, were powered by an auxiliary petrol engine.

Driving positions were provided at both ends and the controllers were arranged to control four motors in series, two sets of motors in series-parallel, and four motors in parallel, and for a maximum speed of 25mph. Weight in working order was 44·25 tons and overall dimensions were: length 33ft 4in, height 12ft 10⅞in, width 8ft 6in over platform and 8ft 8in over roof, bogie wheelbase 5ft 6in; total distance between bogie centres was 15ft and wheel diameter 36in.

Extensive trials made on the Hawthorn Leslie works railway system at Forth Banks showed that the locomotive easily exceeded its expected drawbar pull of 6 tons. The efficiency of the components was estimated at 93 per cent for the generator, traction motors 92 per cent, worm gear 96 per cent, with an overall transmission efficiency of 82 per cent. The works railway at Forth Banks included gradients of 1 in 14 on the straight and 1 in 18 combined with an 'S' curve.

Troubles with the petrol engines, which were not entirely suitable for rail traction, were never overcome and although new engines were desirable none was ever obtained or fitted. The locomotive never left the Forth Banks works and was stored there until 1935 when it was finally dismantled.

To meet an enquiry from an overseas government, a design for a Paragon-type locomotive somewhat similar to No 3500 was prepared by Hawthorn Leslies, based on the trials and research work carried out on the prototype. Planned to fulfill arduous duties on mountain grades under severe operating conditions, it was of the full-length body-type with end driving positions and was carried on articulated, rather than bogie-type, running gear. It was to have had two 150hp six-cylinder petrol engines of the two-stroke type running at 600rpm. These were to be mounted at each end of a centrally placed generator and supply electricity to four traction motors arranged, as on No 3500, to drive one axle each via worm-axle drive units. A thermodynamic efficiency of 30 per cent was anticipated. Control of the engines was by the governor, with master controllers at each end in the cabs for the transmission. Again, for some reason unknown, this locomotive was never built.

The designs of both the above locomotive and No 3500 appear to have incorporated the orthodox transmission system and not the oft-discussed 'Paragon B + B system'. This was a 'mixed' system incorporating storage batteries, which were always kept fully charged using spare generating capacity whilst Paragon locomotives were working on level routes or downhill. They were thus always available to meet extra demands for power, as when starting a train load or when climbing gradients. Durtnall claimed that this allowed smaller and lighter engines to be fited to his locomotives and

it was also possible to use the batteries for driving the locomotive when it was not thought economic to start the main engines, as when running light or doing shunting duties. The main disadvantage of this concept was the bulk and weight of the batteries, and although a standard-gauge pure Paragon battery shunter was built, and used with complete success, as was a similar mining locomotive, none of the mixed type was ever built.

During 1919 Manning Wardle received what was to prove their final order for an internal-combustion locomotive. A delivery date of ten to twelve weeks was quoted but delivery was not made until April 1920, and the locomotive, though bearing Manning Wardle's works No 1996, had in fact been built by Motor Rail & Tram Car Co Ltd at Bedford. A standard product of theirs, it carried their works No 1970.

This 4½ ton, 20hp standard-gauge petrol locomotive with Dorman engine and Simplex transmission was brought to Leeds and sent to its purchaser, The New Tomatin Distillers Co Ltd, Tomatin, Scotland. Motor Rail Ltd supplied a new Dorman petrol/kerosene engine for it in 1940 and the locomotive was scrapped and replaced by a new Motor Rail Simplex locomotive in the mid-1960s. Overall length was 9ft 2in, height 8ft 5¾in, width 7ft, wheelbase 5ft 6in, wheel diameter 24in.

In 1920 The Kent Construction & Engineering Co Ltd of Ashford, Kent, makers of agricultural and light railway equipment, entered the locomotive market, trading under the name of Honeywill Brothers, of London. The availability of large numbers of surplus internal-combustion locomotives after the end of the war was foreseen as the

Fig 28 A post-1920 proposal for a 300hp Paragon locomotive by Hawthorn Leslie for overseas (Narrow gauge)

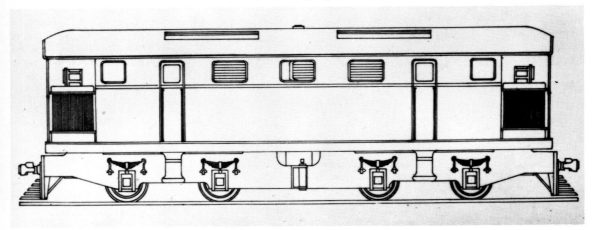

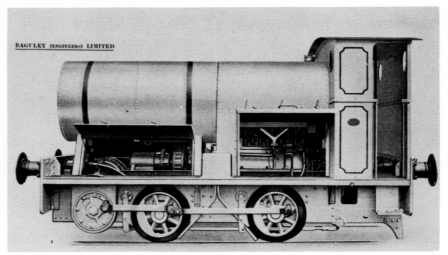

Fig 29 *The Baguley 800 of 1920 which remained unsold for many years until purchased by the London Brick Company. It was laid aside at the firm's Whittlesey works in 1966 and this 100hp machine is now preserved at the Shugborough Hall Museum*

basis for a business, and so Kent Construction purchased numbers of them, mainly narrow-gauge versions of Motor Rail-built Simplex locomotives, and a few of Baldwin locomotive works-type built in the USA. Many of these locomotives had never been used and others were in good condition, while yet others were in varying stages of disrepair or damage. All were purchased, fully overhauled, and offered for resale to contractors and for use in quarries, gravel pits, etc. The ex-WDLR Simplex locomotives were sold under the 'Planet-Simplex' nameplate, and an attempt by Motor Rail Ltd to stop the use of their Simplex trade name failed due to the long delay in applying to the courts. A number of 'pure Planet' petrol locomotives of obvious Simplex parentage, some incorporating Simplex parts, were also sold.

Many pure bow-framed 2½ ton, 20hp petrol locomotives of 'Simplex' type and Motor Rail build which were resold by Kent Construction and their successors had all the cast parts, bearing Simplex identification, removed and replaced by ones carrying Planet nameplates and works numbers. All three ex-WDLR Simplex types, the 2½ ton bow-framed type, the 40hp six-tonner, both 2ft gauge, and the 40hp standard-gauge eight-tonner were offered, the latter forming the basis of the popular 8–10 ton 40hp Planet, in some cases fitted with new superstructures.

Baguley's largest standard-gauge petrol shunter for McEwan Pratt (BG 800) was completed during April 1920 for Dought, Son & Richardson but, due to cancellation of the order, was left on the makers' hands. Powered by a Baguley four-cylinder, 100hp engine running at 1,000rpm, with 6in × 8in cylin-

ders, it had a Baguley patent duplex clutch and a Baguley two-speed, constant-mesh gearbox driving, as was usual in Baguley practice, to transverse drive shaft, with a bevel reverse gearbox mounted across the frames above the final drive jackshaft. The latter was driven by spur gears, and side rods were used to drive the wheels. This large impressive locomotive had the usual cylindrical water tank cooling system over the engine. The transmission was arranged with the engine to the rear, in front of the cab, with the transmission and final drive at the front, all mounted in its own substantial sub-frame.

Finished in lined white livery, the locomotive remained at Shobnall Road works as works shunter until the works closed in 1931. It was finally sold, carrying Baguley (Engineers) Ltd works plates, in June 1933 to the London Brick Company Ltd, Whittlesey, and ended its working days in 1966 at the same firm's Gildenburgh works. In the following year, as the result of strenuous efforts by railway enthusiasts, it was acquired by the Museum of Staffordshire Life, at Shugborough Hall, where it was to be restored as a lasting tribute to the excellence of Baguley's early work in the internal-combustion locomotive field.

Blackstone & Co Ltd of Stamford put on to the market in 1921 an 0-4-0 narrow-gauge petrol locomotive powered by an engine of their own design. This engine, of 25hp, had three cylinders and operated at 750rpm, driving via a three-speed gearbox to a jackshaft final drive unit. The locomotive was quite a substantial design with a long chimney and a full-length overall cab roof supported on pillars, rather like a showman's traction engine. Weight in working order was 3–4 tons, depending on rail gauge and customers' requirements. Overall dimensions were: length 10ft 3in, height 7ft 7in, width 4ft 8in, wheelbase 3ft 3in, wheel diameter 17½in. Speeds were 2·75, 5·6 and 7·5mph. The locomotive was marketed by J. & F. Howard Ltd of Bedford, who were later to build their own locomotives.

A non-standard locomotive type was built in May 1921 by Baguleys for Francis Theakston & Co Ltd of Crewe. Theakstons were light railway equipment suppliers who sold locomotives, usually not of their own build but carrying their trade name of 'Ubique' on the nameplate. As this unit was the first locomotive to be built by Baguleys for other than McEwan Pratt, it is noteworthy. Ordered in December 1919, it was allocated works No 797 in the Baguley list, and was an 0–4–0 petrol unit for 2ft gauge with outside frames. The engine was a 7in × 13in single-cylinder Corbett-Williams horizontal unit giving 10hp at 280rpm, and drove to a transverse shaft with large flywheels to a Baguley duplex clutch. A two-speed gearbox was fitted, driving to spur gear and to a central jackshaft within the locomotive's wheelbase. Overall length (over buffer beams) was 9ft 3¾in, height 7ft 0½in, width 4ft 4in, wheelbase 3ft 3in, wheel diameter 18½in. The speed range was 3·37 and 6 mph. The machine was shipped to Calcutta in 1921.

Four 3ft 6in-gauge 0–4–0 locomotives, ordered from McEwan Pratt for Takoradi Harbour, Gold Coast Colony, were built by Baguley (Cars) Ltd in September and October 1922, carrying works Nos 1278–81. Ordered in March 1922, they were un-

usually fine looking machines, sporting a large, wide-roofed open type tropical cab with double roof, which was overall 2ft 6½in wider than the locomotive itself, the usual Baguley water cooling tank, a shapely brass-capped chimney for the engine exhaust, a sand dome resembling a steam dome in shape and position, a large headlamp, and an engine-exhaust-operated whistle.

They were powered by Baguley four-cylinder engines of 45hp, had a Baguley duplex plate clutch, and the usual spur-driven jackshaft and side rod final drive arrangement of Baguley design and manufacture. Radiator cooling was used in addition to the water tank system. Overall dimensions were: length 11ft 1in, width (excluding cab roof) 5ft 11½in, height 7ft 8in, wheelbase 4ft, wheel diameter 21in. Weight in working order was 6 tons, and speeds 3 and 10mph, with a tractive effort of 3,375lb at 3mph.

Although arousing considerable interest among engineers, it was not perhaps until 1924 at the Wembley Exhibition that the 'mass inertia' or 'wave' transmission system, devised by George Constantinesco, was applied to railway traction. Exhibits at Wembley included a number of models, a small transmission in a road motorcar chassis and, in addition, the frames from an old Great Western Railway outside-framed 0–6–0 goods locomotive, fitted with a six-cylinder petrol engine and the large Constantinesco transmission. The frames were modified to give a 2–4–0 axle arrangement, the third axle arrangement being used to fit a jackshaft drive unit and the pony truck to support that

Fig 30 *A small 25hp 0–4–0*PM *by Blackstone & Co Ltd in 1920–1 (Narrow gauge)*

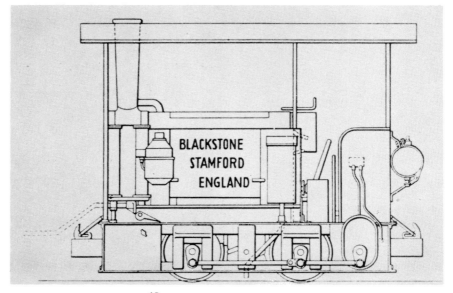

Fig 31 *The amazing Takoradi Harbour Baguley–McEwan Pratt units of 1922. A total of four of these 45hp machines were supplied,* BG *1278–81 (3ft 6in gauge)*

end of the frames. After the exhibition closed, the locomotive was tried on the Southern Railway in Longhedge Yard, Battersea, on shunting and haulage work.

The Constantinesco transmission or torque convertor was basically simple in conception, being based on levers and ratchets, but quite elaborate mathematical descriptions are needed to describe its working principle fully. The system employed a directly driven shaft from the engine which had a driving crank on it connected to the centre of a rocking lever by a connecting rod. The rocking lever was itself pivoted at the lower end to a large pendulum, pivoted at the top, which was allowed

to swing freely. The top of the rocking lever had a further pivot, from which two arms led to the driving or output shaft, to which they were attached ratchet fashion, to engage in the toothed driving shaft end disc. A series of rollers was used to replace the ratchet in the working units. When the engine started to drive the driven shaft the rotation was transmitted to the rocking lever which started the pendulum swinging. The more the pendulum swung, the greater the driven effort.

The locomotive employed a jackshaft final drive unit and, although in principle it was a sound idea, the trouble in trying to accommodate large units within a railway loading gauge, and the inability to

Fig 32 *The Constantinesco shunter of 1924. Seen here on trial at Longhedge Yard, Battersea, on the Southern Railway in 1925*

provide correct balancing and levers of sufficient strength, ruled out any likelihood of success. Nevertheless, the original idea has been revived on numerous occasions as basically sound in principle, but the same problems have always arisen, so keeping the idea in the realm of theory rather than practice.

In April 1923 Baguley (Cars) Ltd re-formed as Baguley (Engineers) Ltd, a name more in keeping with their current activities, which by then included general engineering work, Drewry inspection cars, trolleys, railcars, locomotives for McEwan Pratt, steam locomotives, and light railway rolling stock, to the total exclusion of road vehicles.

In an attempt to provide an economical light industrial shunting locomotive, Lake & Elliot Ltd of Braintree, Essex, introduced during 1923 the prototype of a standard-gauge model. The design was very simple and the locomotive portion, which was built at the Braintree works, consisted of a flat-topped underframe based on railway wagon practice with four wheels and enough weight for effective adhesion. A chain drive was fitted to both axles from the transverse drive shaft under the flat top. The power plant, a standard Fordson tractor with wheels removed, was simply lowered into position and connected to the gearing to drive the wheels. The haulage power was sufficient for a 90 ton load and the whole locomotive, complete with tractor, cost £300 or, without tractor, £120. The original locomotive is still in use at Hoffmans, Lake & Elliot's successors.

Nelson Corporation Gas Department in Lancashire took delivery during 1923 of the first internal-combustion locomotive to be built by John Fowler & Co (Leeds) Ltd. This 0-4-0 petrol machine (JF 16038) was a simple, straightforward type with jackshaft and side rod drive, and was of 35hp. Rebuilt with a new AEC diesel engine and a bus-type AEC radiator, this locomotive was noted in use in 1965 by the firm of W. Bush & Sons Ltd, Alfreton, who were engaged on lifting the Woodburn branch line in Northumberland. The locomotive has recently been purchased for preservation.

W. G. Bagnall Ltd built one small 3ft-gauge petrol locomotive similar to No P50 of 1914 for the Eastern Assam Co Ltd. It was works No 2220 and had a Ford engine.

The re-entry of Avonside Engine Co Ltd into the internal-combustion field was marked by the building of five locomotives for Francis Theakston & Co Ltd of Crewe during 1923-4. Allotted Avonside works Nos 1915/24-7, they were 0-4-0 units of 2ft-gauge, carrying Theakston plates with their trade name 'Ubique'. They were fitted with Corbett Williams single-cylinder horizontal engines of 7in × 13in bore and stroke, rated at 11·5hp at 280rpm. The engine drove on to a transverse shaft with a 3ft 6in diameter flywheel at the left-hand side, driving to a Baguley duplex clutch. A two-speed gearbox giving speeds of 3·36 and 7mph drove to a central jackshaft with spur drive. The locomotives were of the same design as Baguley 797 of 1921 and, in the case of locomotives 1924/5

Fig 33 *Fowler's first petrol locomotive —a 1923 product for the Nelson Corporation Gasworks in Lancashire,* JF *16038/23*

Fig 34 *An Avonside-built 11hp locomotive for Theakstons in 1923. AE 1924 and 1925 of 2ft gauge for Hadfields, Staffs*

and 1926/7, were supplied to Hadfields Ltd, Staffordshire, and Belfast Corporation, but the disposal of locomotive 1915 is not known.

In 1923 Hawthorn Leslies completed for experimental service at their Forth Banks works a very unusual locomotive, based on the underframe of one of the firm's standard industrial 0–6–0ST steam locomotives with outside cylinders. This machine, works No 3513, was a 'Paragon-Cristiani' locomotive with compressed steam transmission—yet another attempt to obtain the starting power of steam, coupled with the efficiency of an internal-combustion prime mover. The idea was to cut out the locomotive boiler, the most costly component of steam traction, but at the same time to retain the steam locomotive cylinders and running gear so that, if successful, existing steam locomotives might be easily adapted to the system by removal of the boiler.

Although the Italian, Cristiani, originated the idea, it seems that W. P. Durtnall was in charge of the work and indeed later patented a combined internal-combustion engine and compressor for use in such locomotives. Further work was done in Italy by Cristiani on a larger scale.

The Hawthorn Leslie locomotive had two cylinders, 14in diameter × 22in stroke, coupled wheels of 42in diameter, overall length of 23ft and a weight of 43 tons in running order. The power equipment was housed in a full-length, full-width, overall superstructure with driving positions at both ends, and comprised a vee type, six-cylinder compressor driven by two reconditioned six-cyl-

inder, 160hp at 450rpm, marine petrol engines similar to those used in the thermo-electric Paragon locomotive, a small oil-fired steam boiler, and low- and high-pressure steam reservoirs.

The principle of the system was that the locomotive was started using the low-pressure steam generated by the oil-fired boiler. The petrol engines were then started and steam was drawn from the low-pressure reservoir, ready for use in the locomotive cylinders after being compressed and fed by the compressor into the high-pressure reservoir. The compressed steam, after use in the cylinders, was returned to the low-pressure reservoir. The available useful working pressure was equal to the difference in pressure between the low- and high-pressure sides of the system.

The experiment was fairly successful, but difficulties in maintaining sufficient pressure difference between the two sides of the system when the locomotive was working presented a problem. In an attempt to overcome this a steam accumulator in the form of a standard fireless locomotive steam receiver was added to the system. This was towed behind the unit on a four-wheeled flat wagon. This addition, providing from its water steam raised to the locomotive's working pressure, made a big improvement in operation. There was always enough heat in the reservoir to enable the locomotive to deal with peak loads, and it could be replenished when the unit was operating down gradients or over level sections of line. Additional heat was taken from the petrol engines themselves for the high-pressure steam reservoir, using possibly the

Fig 35 *The 'Paragon–Cristiani' compressed steam locomotive by Hawthorn Leslie built in 1923 for experimental purposes,* HL 3513/23

Fig 36 *The compressed-steam locomotive operating with an additional steam reservoir tender*

Fig 37 *A 1926 8-ton 40hp Planet petrol locomotive based on Simplex practice for Worthington's Brewery, Burton-on-Trent*

patent 'Paragon heat transfer equipment' of Durt-nall's invention.

The system worked quite well and the only trouble experienced was with the petrol engines, which were not entirely suitable for railway use. The locomotive was dismantled and the frames re-used as a standard 0–6–0ST (HL 3513/27), named *Stagshaw* and supplied to Strakers & Love Ltd, Brancepeth Colliery, County Durham. As such, it was still in use until mid 1972 at the Shotton Colliery of the National Coal Board, being subsequently preserved.

Possibly through their connections with the Distillers Co Ltd, the brothers, Ross and Constantine Honeywill, delivered during the 1924–6 period a number of Planet shunting locomotives to the Burton-on-Trent brewery of Worthington & Co Ltd. These locomotives were built by Kent Construction & Engineering Co Ltd at Ashford and were standard-gauge machines of 8 tons weight, carried on two axles. Very similar to Motor Rail Ltd-built Simplex locomotives, they may, as previously intimated, have incorporated many Simplex parts or even have been Simplex ex-WD and ROD locomotives, fitted with new superstructures.

The engines were transversely mounted and were Dorman 40hp units driving to a gearbox and with chain drive to both axles. They were 13ft 6in over buffers, 10ft 3in high, 7ft 8½in wide, had a 5ft 6in wheelbase and 37in diameter wheels. Speeds were 3, 7·2 and 9mph and maximum tractive effort was 3,650lb. A few more followed after the Planet business was acquired by F. C. Hibberd & Co Ltd.

Two locomotives, of similar design to their 1915

War Office petrol locomotives, were supplied by Hawthorn Leslies to the Engineering Company of Portugal or, to give it its full name, Engineering Co, Compania do Buzi of Portugal Ltd, in 1924 and 1928. These were 1ft 11⅝in gauge 0–4–0 units with FHM alcohol engines with four cylinders rated at 50hp. A disc friction clutch, three-speed gearbox, worm axle drive and side-rod coupled wheels formed the transmission. Weight in working order was 8·85 tons, and overall dimensions were: length 15ft 7in, height 9ft 4in, width 6ft, wheelbase 5ft, wheel diameter 27in. The first one (HL 3587/24) was named *Christina* and the second (HL 3727/28), delivered in June 1928, *Beira*.

It was about this time that Kent Construction & Engineering Co Ltd built its first longitudinally engined locomotive, as opposed to the transverse Simplex-derived design. These were simple two-axle petrol units for narrow-gauge use and were the first true Planet locomotives. Powers, weights and rail gauge were adjusted to suit customers' requirements and the typical 10hp, 1¾ tons type had a Dorman four-cylinder engine with a transmission incorporating a standard foot-operated, friction clutch, a two-speed gearbox with bevel reverse, transmission by roller chains to a central countershaft and chains to each pair of wheels. Overall dimensions were: length 8ft 5in, height 4ft 4in, width 4ft, wheelbase 4ft, wheel diameter 15in; maximum tractive effort was 850lb.

One of this design was exhibited at the Public Works, Roads & Transport Congress at Islington in November 1925 by Honeywill Bros Ltd of Ashford and London, who were the people behind the

Fig 38 *A Hawthorn Leslie 50hp 0–4–0PM exported to Portugal in 1924, HL 3587/24 (1ft 11½in gauge). This design was very similar to the War Office design of 1915, HL 3107–29*

Kent Construction Planet locomotive business. Examples were supplied to many firms, quarry and sand pits, etc, two long-lived examples being those at A. P. C. M. Murston Brickworks, Sittingbourne, Kent.

Bagnalls supplied four small petrol locomotives to Norton Griffiths & Co Ltd for oilfield use, all of which were shipped to Maracaibo. Carrying works Nos 2273–5 and 2304, they were 0–4–0 petrol units of 2ft 6in gauge with two-speed gearboxes. No 2273/25 had a 20hp Ford four-cylinder engine while Nos 2274/5 of 1925 had 40hp Dorman four-cylinder engines, as had No 2304/26.

The Bedford firm of James & Frederick Howard Ltd, Britannia Ironworks, had for many years been suppliers of light railway equipment and rolling stock, along with their other activities as agricultural engineers and steam traction engine makers; they also supplied locomotives, though not of their own manufacture. The fact that the Blackstone locomotive was sold by Howards during the early 1920s probably prompted them to enter the market on their own account with locomotives fitted with petrol engines and built at their own works. The first designs were narrow-gauge units built with Howard's own design of underframe, which was quite simple but very sound and rigid in construction. The frame was constructed from rolled steel sections built as an open box, bolted together and strongly braced. The box-type frame permitted maximum accessibility. The transmission and the running gear incorporated full use of roller bearings.

The engines used were 20–8hp Morris four-cylinder petrol units. The transmission included a two-speed and reverse gearbox which drove to a countershaft from which a roller chain drove

to the front axle, and from there another chain drove the rear axle. Engine and transmission were mounted complete on their own subframe, which was then attached to the complete underframe.

This type of locomotive was the 'S' type and was available in gauges 1ft 4in–2ft and in weights of 2, 2½ and 3 tons. Overall dimensions were: length 9ft 7in, height 5ft 3in, or 6ft 6in with cab, width 3ft 7½in, or 4ft with cab, wheelbase 3ft 3in, wheel diameter 18in.

The larger Howard design, the type 'H', was similar in design but was powered by a 31–48hp four-cylinder petrol engine, and the weight range was 3, 4, 5 and 6 tons for rail gauges 60cm–3ft 6in. Overall dimensions differed slightly—length 10ft 1in, height 5ft 4¾in, or 7ft with cab, width 3ft 11in, or 4ft 6½in with cab, wheelbase 3ft 11in, wheel diameter 18in. Both the 'S' and 'H' types were later available with Blackstone oil engines.

A derivative of the 'H' type was the steep haulage type locomotive with patent adhesion wheel. Produced in an attempt to provide a simple method of increasing the usefulness of locomotives over steeply graded lines, as encountered in civil engineering contracts, etc, the locomotive was fitted with a fifth wheel arrangement. The auxiliary adhesion wheel was centrally situated behind the rear wheels and was lowered to run on a centrally placed wooden track between the rails. The wheel had rubber tyres and was twined with a driving sprocket in the middle, driven off the rear axle by a chain. The wheel had ball bearings and was on a fixed axle with eccentric adjustments between the hornplates, similar to those of the other axles. A cast-steel yoke straddled the auxiliary wheel and was fixed to the axle, above which a strong helical spring was arranged in a column

Fig 39 A typical Kent Construction-built 10hp Planet as supplied to Murston Brickworks, Sittingbourne, Kent (2ft gauge)

Fig 40 *The Howard type 'H' 4WPM of 31–48hp working at a cement works in the South-East. The type 'S' was similar. An example has been preserved (2ft gauge)*

alongside the driver. A fine pitch screw was provided to put it under compression and thus transfer part of the locomotive's weight on to the auxiliary wheel. Overall length was 8in greater than the standard 'H' type design and the weight was 3½ tons, but otherwise details were identical. The auxiliary wheel was 16in in diameter with tyres 3½in wide on the treads. The speeds were 3·16 and 8·15mph.

Although widely evaluated and demonstrated, very few examples were built, and only one may actually have been sold—to John J. Shardlow & Co Ltd, public works contractors of Leicester, who used a steep haulage locomotive, together with other Howards, on their Abbey pumping station contracts at Leicester.

Shortly afterwards, Howards introduced their range of larger petrol shunters designed for gauges from 3ft to 5ft 6in, and in the weight range of 7, 10 and 12 tons. All were two-axle designs and were highly standardised, being based on a similar mechanical portion to the narrow-gauge designs. The 7 ton unit had a 41–8hp four-cylinder petrol engine and a two-speed gearbox with final drive by chains. Overall dimensions were: length 15ft, height over cab 8ft 2in, width 7ft 7in, wheelbase 4ft 9in, wheel diameter 18in.

The 10 and 12 ton locomotives were identical, apart from the engine sizes and outputs; the 10 ton locomotive had a 45–57hp four-cylinder engine and the 12-tonner a 61–80hp six-cylinder Dorman unit. The transmission incorporated a three-speed gearbox, giving maximum speeds of 10 and 11·15 mph respectively. They had an overall length of 17ft 10in, height over cab was 9ft 6in, width 7ft 7in, wheelbase 5ft 6in, wheel diameter 30in.

A 7 ton locomotive is preserved on the Bluebell Railway and one 12 ton locomotive remained at Wiggins Teape Ltd, Ford Paper Mill, Sunderland, County Durham, which has now been preserved at Lytham Creek Museum through the generosity of Wiggins Teape Ltd.

The following tables show the haulage capacity of the design as compared with the standard 'H' type locomotive.

STANDARD 'H' TYPE LOCOMOTIVE
At engine speed 1,000rpm

	On slow gear 3·16mph	On fast gear 8·15mph
	Gross load	Gross load
Gradient	(tons)	(tons)
Level	60	35
1 in 100	30	17
1 in 60	20	12
1 in 40	16	9
1 in 20	8	4

STEEP HAULAGE TYPE LOCOMOTIVE
At engine speed 1,000rpm

	Slow gear (3·16mph)	
	Adhesion wheel not in use	Adhesion wheel in operation
	Gross load	Gross load
Gradient	(tons)	(tons)
Level	70	85
1 in 100	35	44
1 in 60	25	32
1 in 40	18	23
1 in 20	10	12
1 in 15	—	9
1 in 12	—	7

Fig 41 *A 7-ton Howard of 41–8hp shunting at the maker's Bedford works in 1926. The 10–12-ton design was similar and an example of each is preserved on the Bluebell Railway and at the Lytham Creek Museum*

During 1925 the name of McEwan Pratt ceased to be used on Baguley-built locomotives, and abandonment of this name, so well known for its quality of product, was to bode ill in later years for Baguleys. From this time, mid-1925, all locomotives built by Baguley (Engineers) Ltd were sold under the Drewry Car Co's nameplate and from their offices.

Crossley Brothers Ltd of Manchester took over the Bedford works of the Saunderson Tractor & Implement Co Ltd (the successors of Saunderson & Gifkins Ltd) in 1925. In so doing they entered the locomotive manufacturing business for one year only, in that there were in hand at the Elstow works three petrol locomotives for Beswicks Limeworks Ltd, Hindlow, Derbyshire; it is doubtful if any more were built. Two were 2ft-gauge machines weighing 5 tons and fitted with 25hp Crossley engines. Transmission was via a two-speed, $3\frac{1}{4}$ and 7mph, constant mesh gearbox with final drive by chains. They were 10ft 6in long and 7ft 6in high, with a maximum haulage capacity of 70 tons. The third locomotive was a very similar standard-gauge locomotive, about which little is known.

Fig 42 *One of Beswick's Limeworks three Crossley units of 1925. This example is one of the two 2ft-gauge units*

Fig 43 *The Hardy Railmotors/*FWD *locomotive of 4ft gauge on the Dinorwic Quarries Padarn Railway at Llanberis. This last British example was scrapped in 1963*

After the end of World War I, disposal of vast amounts of equipment was facilitated by various companies which were set up to offer for resale, after suitable modification or reconstruction, such items as road vehicles and various other types of powered plant. One item in plentiful supply was the ex-army FWD or four wheel drive petrol motor lorry, which a company at Slough, trading as Four Wheel Drive Motors Ltd and with a works on the trading estate, was set up to remarket in various ways. They were approached by Major-General C. L. Holden, who was interested in a patent to produce a convertible road–rail vehicle and saw the ex-army FWD lorry as a basis for this. Its wheel spacing was almost to the standard rail gauge of 4ft 8½in, and the fact that Four Wheel Drive Motors could do the conversion, and market the result, was an attractive possibility. Holden's vehicle was a very simple conversion with interchangeable wheel tyres of steel for rail, and solid rubber for road. Nothing much appears to have been done with Holden's idea, but before long tests were under way with just such a vehicle, said to be the result of work by Four Wheel Drive Motors themselves. It was convertible for rail or road use and extensive trials were carried out during 1923 at Slough trading estate. This prototype was still a lorry, with a front-facing driving position at the front only. It also retained the wagon body, and had only light buffing gear.

This was offered for sale, but Mr C. F. Cleaver, the managing director and chief designer, set about to produce a unit specifically for railway use, which, although using standard lorry components,

such as engine and axles, was built much more robustly. It had a far stronger chassis, heavier but shorter, and improved springing and buffing gear. One of the very first examples of this unit, which had a wooden cab and rear wagon type body, was supplied to the Derwent Valley Light Railway at York in 1923. From experience with this type, the production model was developed, and this, to avoid confusion with the road lorries, was to be marketed by a subsidiary company, Hardy Railmotors Ltd.

Although a standard-type four-cylinder petrol engine was used, the locomotive was available in the 40–70hp range and had a transmission incorporating a Hele-Shaw multiple-disc clutch running in oil, and sliding dog jaw constant-mesh gearbox giving four speeds. All shafts and gears ran on ball- and roller-bearings. The drive was by cardan shafts to both axles which were driven independently by bevel gear axle drive units. The axles were of the full floating type with the running wheels carried on large diameter tapered roller bearings. The speed range was 2·6, 4, 8 and 16mph via the main gearbox and this was obtained in both directions by using a separate subsidiary reversing gearbox, fitted between the clutch and the main gearbox. Braking was by drums on each wheel operated by a screw-down hand brake, while an additional drum brake was fitted on the transmission at the back of the gearbox, giving an effective four-wheel braking system.

This modified type followed the design of the DVLR unit, in that, to permit visibility for travel in both directions, the driver sat sideways, and to obviate cooling troubles, radiators were provided at either end of the locomotive. The cab was, however, centrally placed and the bodywork, although still of wood, was covered in steel sheet to give improved appearance, space being provided behind the cab for ballast weights. Some versions were fitted with power take-off points to operate pumps etc, while on others, a wire rope winch was installed. With a heavier chassis and stronger axles and springs, the locomotive weight could be taken to 12 tons with ballasting.

The locomotive was 19ft 2in over buffers, with a length over headstocks of 16ft 2in. The wheelbase was 8ft 5in and the diameter of the pressed steel disc wheels 33½in. Examples were sold to United Dairies, the Air Ministry, Kingsnorth Light Railway, and various industrial users. The 4ft-gauge Swansea & Mumbles Railway also had one, the final survivor of this gauge being on the Dinorwic Quarries Padarn Railway, Llanberis, but this was scrapped in 1963. Versions were also supplied as fire engines and inspection cars, while passenger versions went to the Spurn Point Railway and to a railway in South America.

Hardy Railmotors became part of AEC (Associated Equipment Company Ltd) and in due course the Slough works closed down. Operations continued, however, from the AEC works at Southall as that firm's Hardy Motors Division. They were the designers of the first GWR diesel railcars, though eventually the name was dropped around 1936, thus ending the story of Hardy Railmotors.

About 1923 the Slough trading company built (or caused to be built by Hardys?) a four-wheel petrol shunter using old army tank parts. This unit, of very professional appearance, was designed by Mr J. A. Boyd. It was not a commercially sold design and is, therefore, only mentioned for the record.

CHAPTER 6

1926-1929: DIESEL-STEAM AND SOME LARGE LOCOMOTIVES

MUIR HILL, a name familiar in earth-moving equipment and contractors' plant today, entered the small locomotive market in 1926 with a narrow-gauge contractors'-type locomotive. Built for gauges from 2ft, it was a two-axle type powered by a Fordson four-cylinder engine running on paraffin. The transmission included a Muir Hill patent two-speed, 2½ and 7mph gearbox and reverse, with non-crash instantaneous gears, or synchromesh. Drive was via a worm unit and worm wheel to twin sprockets and to front and rear axles by chains, both axles being chain-coupled. The locomotive weighed 4 tons and its overall dimensions were: length 9ft, height 5ft, or 7ft 6in with cab, width 3ft 6in, wheelbase 3ft 2in, wheel diameter 20in. The Ravenglass & Eskdale Railway operates several 15in versions.

An identically powered standard-gauge unit was subsequently built, also weighing 6¼ tons. This was a two-axle type and overall dimensions were: length 13ft 7in, height 9ft 8in, width 6ft 9in, wheelbase 5ft 5½in, wheel diameter 36in.

The Kent Construction & Engineering Co Ltd closed their Ashford works during 1926 and upon the death of Ross Honeywill the business was sold to Messrs F. C. Hibberd and D. A. Dwyer, directors of Honeywill Brothers Ltd of Mark Lane, London. In July 1927 the new firm of F. C. Hibberd & Co Ltd was incorporated with offices in Great Tower Street, London, and the Planet business continued—to become one of the oldest surviving British internal-combustion locomotive manufacturers of high quality industrial locomotives, of world-wide repute.

F. C. Hibberd & Co Ltd acquired the Planet business and the stock of petrol locomotives and tractors at the Ashford works and arranged with Stableford & Co Ltd, wagon builders, of Coalville, Leicestershire, to act as subcontractors and build Planet locomotives under supervision.

It was about this time that Planet were advertising through Honeywill Brothers a 20 ton, two-axle petrol-electric locomotive of French design. Powered by a 90hp Panhard–Levassor four-cylinder sleeve valve engine, coupled to a 52kW generator, it had two traction motors driving the axles by roller chains. The locomotive was designed by Gaston Moyse of Paris and, though it seems unlikely that any were actually built under the Planet nameplate, a few imported models may have been sold.

Kitson & Co Ltd, old-established locomotive builders at Leeds, were among the several British firms who started to think in terms of internal-combustion locomotives during the 1920s. Well aware of experience to date with various forms of internal combustion traction, it was obvious to them that nothing was to be gained with direct-drive diesel locomotives, nor with compressed air-diesel systems. Work on mechanical transmissions for high power, also hydraulic types, was still not sufficiently advanced and this, together with a lack of materials suited to the reliability required of railway locomotives, prompted a study of the electrical transmission system, or diesel-electric locomotive. But here it was felt that the complication, cost and weight of available equipment were such as to offer no practical solution to the problem, nor any promise at that time of becoming a serious rival to steam traction.

The ideal that Kitsons were seeking was a prime mover with the basic ruggedness of steam locomotion, but cheaper to run and maintain, and capable of starting a load at full power. At the same time it had to provide the acknowledged efficiency of the oil engine, as compared to steam, but without the complication of the intricate transmission systems then deemed necessary. All these were highly desirable, but were they attainable?

The Still Engine Co Ltd was then brought to Kitson's attention as a company offering a combined system using both steam and combustion in a common cylinder. A number of stationary Still-type engines had been built and tested at their works at Chiswick. The idea was taken up by Kitsons at an unfortunate time, during the depression of the late 1920s, but in due course the Kitson–Still diesel-steam locomotive was born at great cost, both to the firm's finances and in time spent on experimentation.

This unique machine—Kitson 5374/27—was completed and tested on rollers at Kitson's Airedale works in 1927. It looked very much like a 2–6–2 tank locomotive, without tanks and with inside cylinders, and its external appearance afforded no clue to its connection with diesel traction. It was started by steam made available in the cylindrical boiler with circular firebox by oil-burning equipment. When under way, the steam was generated by waste heat from the combustion or diesel side of the system, namely heat from the water-cooled cylinders, which were connected to the boiler water system, and the diesel exhaust gases which were led through the boiler tubes prior to their release into the atmosphere.

The propulsion unit comprised an eight-cylinder horizontal engine arranged with banks of four cylinders each side of a crankshaft, mounted across the frames but in between. This crankshaft was set slightly above and between the first two driving axles. Directly below the crankshaft was a final drive unit driven by double helical gears which was in the form of a jackshaft within the wheelbase. This in turn drove the wheels by coupling rods, all three axles being coupled.

The working cycle was that steam was used first in the unique eight-cylinder engine, being distributed only to the inner ends of the cylinders by Hackworth gear. The outer ends of the cylinders were used for the diesel side and brought in after the train was under way by airless injection of fuel oil, controlled by the usual roller and cam valves. The whole worked on a four-stroke cycle. Diesel-only working continued but steam could again be brought in for climbing gradients to boost the locomotive's power, and both steam and diesel could be used simultaneously in the system.

Trials began after the locomotive had been exhibited at Leeds in April 1928, and were carried out in the Hunslet goods yard and on trips to Ardsley and back. Then followed runs with coal trains between Darlington and Barnard Castle. Driver-training proved simple and soon LNER men

were ready to undertake supervised service trials on freight trains between York and Hull, both via Market Weighton, and via Church Fenton and Selby in 1932–3. Photographs showing the locomotive on passenger stock exist, but whether these were for trials or service is not known.

The extensive trials included runs with dynamometer cars, the locomotive always performing well and never once failing to complete a run. On typical runs the locomotive started and ran on steam until 6mph was reached, when steam was turned off and diesel brought in, the heat being used to keep up the boiler pressure without the aid of the oil burner. The steam side was brought in as required to boost the train up banks and to restart from stops.

After initial troubles with water contamination of the sump oil of the crank case, due to leaks caused by unequal boiler expansion and also lubrication troubles, the unit performed reasonably well in service, bearing in mind its unique design, and was developed into a reliable machine in the course of some six years of running and trials.

Tentative plans for a further model had to be abandoned when work stopped owing to financial difficulties attributable to the slump, withdrawal of capital and the vast sums spent on the locomotive which had not created much interest among railways still wedded to steam traction. Kitsons, after being in receivership since 1934, closed in 1938 and the locomotive was subsequently dismantled, having arrived before its time. Main dimensions were: length over buffers 39ft 6in, height 13ft 1in, total wheelbase 28ft 3in, coupled wheelbase 14ft 3in, wheel diameter 60in. The eight cylinders had $13\frac{1}{2}$in bore × $15\frac{1}{2}$in stroke. Weight in working order was 87 tons, and it carried 400gal of fuel oil and 1,000gal of water in bunkers behind the cab.

Diverging briefly from the British situation to record what was being achieved elsewhere, we see that in the USA some early work by General Electric with a few low-powered locomotives using Junkers' engines built under licence, was in progress. In Germany, Maybach's low-powered engines of high-speed type were stimulating thought. Although contrary to British practice, notably Beardmore's, Maybach persisted with air-blast fuel injection up to 1930, as opposed to the superior airless solid-fuel injection systems now universally adopted.

In Russia, the mid-1920s saw the introduction of the Lomonossoff 1–Eo–1 diesel-electric. This 124-ton, 1,200hp MAN submarine-engined unit,

Fig 44 *The Kitson–Still diesel-steam locomotive on test in the Kitson works in 1926*

running at 450rpm, built up a high mileage on slow freight train work. This and the similar 2–E–1 diesel mechanical 1,200hp unit were started by the old locomotive builders in Germany, Hohenzollern, but were completed by Maschinenfabrik Esslingen after the original firm closed down from lack of orders. Krupps was concerned with the mechanical transmission of the latter locomotive.

Low-powered work on railcars and shunters was now becoming common and Sulzers did much good work up to 400hp in this field. The first line service unit from Sulzers was ordered in 1925 and delivered the following year to Tunisian Railways in North Africa. This was a 250hp Bo-Bo diesel-electric. It was still in service after World War II.

In the USA, railcar work was also in progress, but it was probably the work of Herman Lemp with American General Electric which set that continent on its way to successful locomotives. Lemp designed an engine for GE, got Ingersoll-Rand to build it and by 1924 had it installed in a 300hp diesel-electric shunter; soon 600–800hp locomotives were being built by GE. Lemp's work with electrical transmission and control systems has never been fully recognised and the fact that his ideas achieved world-wide implementation made this contribution more important than his engine work.

Other work of the 1920s, again stemming from Europe, was the Japanese National Railways' 1–C–1 diesel-electric of 1929 by Maschinenfabrik Esslingen with a 600hp MAN engine, and Brown–Boveri electrics, using jackshaft and side-rod final drive. Some similar examples were built in Japan,

and Krupp in 1931 supplied a unit somewhat akin to this with mechanical transmission and a 600hp Krupp engine. None of these locomotives survived the war.

Frichs of Aarhus, Denmark, were in the forefront at this period and delivered in 1929 two 450hp 2–Bo–1 units to Danish State Railways, which survived to be re-engined after the war.

Since 1925 the railway foundry of Hudswell Clarke at Leeds had been building a few small petrol locomotives of narrow-gauge type for contractors and plantations. These locomotives, starting in a new works number list from P251 of 1925, were built up to the early 1930s, when the diesel locomotive came to the fore. P261, a small two-axle unit with outside frames, was of special interest because it was Hudswell's first diesel locomotive, being shipped via Rangoon during November 1927 for service with a timber company, and ordered through Milne & Co Ltd of London. It was powered by a McLaren–Benz lightweight engine of 30hp running at 800rpm. An auxiliary petrol engine was installed for starting and it had a two-speed gearbox with final drive by chains.

Andrew Barclay, Sons & Co Ltd built their seventh internal-combustion locomotive in 1927 for the agent general of Western Australia. This 3ft 6in gauge 0–4–0 petrol locomotive was powered by a 40hp Dorman 4JO four-cylinder engine. The transmission included a multiple-plate clutch and two-speed gearbox giving speeds of 3 and 6mph. A flexible coupling connected the clutch to the gearbox and drive was then through a double bevel reverse gear to a transverse shaft geared to the final drive jackshaft, side rod drive being used. Weight in working order was 6½ tons, and overall dimensions were: length over buffer beams 14ft, height 10ft 1½in, width 5ft 5½in, wheelbase 4ft, wheel diameter 24½in. It was works No 317 of 1927.

Motor Rail & Tram Car Co Ltd of Bedford were still supplying hundreds of their highly standardised locomotives, mainly for narrow-gauge duties, but they did supply numbers of their 8–10 ton standard-gauge type for industrial shunting work, and to the mainline railways. Developed from the World War I type, they proved very popular for light work and most of the British mainline railways purchased some, which they tended to use for service and departmental duties. Used by the pre-grouping railways such as the North British Railway, Great Eastern Railway, Lancashire & Yorkshire Railway, and later by the GWR and LNER, a number survived to become nationalised under British Railways.

Powered by 40hp Dorman four-cylinder petrol engines, they had Motor Rail patent transmissions with inverted cone clutch in a large diameter flywheel, a two-speed, 3 and 7mph gearbox and heavy roller chain drives to each axle. Overall dimensions were: length 13ft 4in, height 10ft 7in, width 7ft 7in, wheelbase 5ft 6in, wheel diameter 37in, and a maximum tractive effort of 3,750lb.

During 1928–9 a number of manufacturers turned their attention to the production of small contractors'-type internal-combustion locomotives, stimulated no doubt by the profusion of small continental products being sold in Britain by British dealers and agents. One of these, The Standard Steel Co Ltd of Croydon, agents for Jung locomotives and makers of light railway equipment, produced a range of small two-axle contractors' loco-

motives based to a large extent on one of the Jung designs but entirely British in manufacture.

The 'Stansteco Minor' was powered by a Trojan four-cylinder, two-stroke petrol engine. The transmission was a single-plate clutch, constant mesh two-speed gearbox, giving speeds of 5 and 12mph, gear selection being by dog clutches. Final drive was by chain to one axle, both axles being chain coupled. The Minor had a 2ft 7½in wheelbase and sold for £185. The 'Stansteco Major' had a 10hp single-cylinder two-stroke diesel engine with the same transmission as the Minor and cost £285. They were built for gauges 1ft 6in–3ft but only a few were sold, two to a 'Cambridgeshire public body', which later purchased two more, one to Cornwall, one to Lancashire, and a few others, as yet not definitely traced.

D. Wickham & Co Ltd of Ware, Hertfordshire, did a small amount of contractors' locomotive work around this time, in addition to their usual activity of building railcars, inspection cars and trolleys. One of the first of their designs, totalling about five up to 1936, was a 2 ton, two-axle type with a 20hp four-cylinder Morris engine. Its transmission was via a constant mesh two-speed gearbox with sliding dog clutches; chain drive was provided to both axles. It was 7ft 3in in length, had a wheelbase of 2ft 6in with 16in diameter wheels and a speed range of 3–6mph. This was followed by the 'E type' with a 25–30hp four-cylinder petrol engine and similar transmission.

Another one, type R597 for gauges 2ft 6in–5ft 6in, was built with either a 20–24hp two-cylinder diesel engine or a 26–50hp four-cylinder petrol engine. The transmission was a dry multiple-plate clutch with diesel or inverted cone with petrol, a

Fig 45 *The Stansteco Minor* 4WPM *contractors' locomotive of 1928–9; a diesel version, the Major, was also produced. (2ft gauge)*

standard Wickham two-speed, 3 and 6mph gearbox, an oil bath bevel gear drive with roller bearings and roller chains to an intermediate shaft, with further roller chains to each axle. Yet another one, type DW3 of 1935, had a weight of 2–4 tons and a JAP petrol engine of 14hp at 1,500rpm, a five-speed gearbox being fitted. One of the final designs appears to have been a two-axle unit with a two-cylinder 8–18hp diesel engine dating from around 1936. This example was 8ft 9in in overall length, 7ft 4in high over cab, had a wheelbase of 2ft 10in and the usual 16in diameter wheels. Very few examples of each type were built, in some instances only prototypes, and no record appears to survive of their purchasers or their subsequent fate.

Robert Hudson Ltd, long-standing railway equipment manufacturers, who had previously sold other builders' locomotives (notably Kerr Stuarts; Hudswell Clarke; and Hunslets) in many cases carrying Hudson works plates, turned their attention around 1928 to marketing a light petrol locomotive range of their own. Although producing rolling stock of all types and gauges, the firm's Gildersome works near Leeds does not appear to have built these locomotives, which were apparently supplied to Hudsons by Thomas Green & Sons of Leeds, a firm now noted for agricultural and road-making equipment but who did some steam locomotive work at one time.

The Hudson locomotives bore some resemblance to contemporary work of Muir Hill and Lake & Elliot, being based largely on the engine and transmission of the Fordson tractor, which was placed in the simply constructed chassis. A number of the two basic designs offered were sold, the narrow-gauge example weighing 4 tons, and the standard-gauge unit 6 tons. The production life was short, for the coming availability of the more robust Kerr Stuart and, later, Hunslet diesel locomotives was soon taken advantage of, and the well-known Hudson–Hunslet light diesel locomotive ranges are now well established.

Another Francis Theakston order was carried out during 1928 by the Avonside Engine Co Ltd. This locomotive was a 2ft-gauge 0–4–0 petrol/paraffin unit and was, as far as Avonsides were concerned, a 'one off' job. Bearing Avonside works No 1980, it was powered by a 40hp Brotherhood–Ricardo engine which drove via a three-speed gearbox and chain drive to the leading axle, both axles being rod coupled. It had a wheelbase of 3ft 6in, wheels of 27in diameter and a speed range of 3, 7 and 11mph; it was supplied to British Phosphate Ltd and sent overseas.

The return of Kerr Stuart to the diesel locomotive market occurred in 1928, when a new highly standardised locomotive range was introduced. The range was produced and marketed with success under the direction of W. K. Willans, who had previously been with the Sentinel Wagon Works Ltd at Shrewsbury, and largely responsible for the successful Sentinel geared high-pressure steam engines used in locomotives, railcars and road vehicles. With so much experience, Willans produced at Stoke-on-Trent a basic narrow-gauge range of locomotives, powered by either diesel or high-pressure steam engines and using a common underframe, running gear and final drive unit. Two- and three-axle varieties were built and it was a simple matter to accommodate a number of rail gauges simply by changing the wheel-axle sets.

Although mainly diesel-powered locomotives were built, a few steam examples were supplied and worked successfully. The locomotives were built on a stock basis so that orders could be quickly met. In all cases the McLaren engine was used and 30, 60 and 90hp locomotives were built. The gearbox and final drive units built by Kerr Stuart, using David Brown bevel wheels and spur gears, were located at the front of the locomotive, driving to the axles by roller chains. The 60 and 90hp models had JAP petrol-starting engines fitted.

The first example, KS 4415, was completed in 1928 and used as a demonstration locomotive. This 60hp 10½ ton unit was tried on the Welsh Highland Railway from July 1928 and then on the Festiniog Railway in March 1929, who returned it to Stoke in August 1929, having used it on a wide range of duties. It was lent to Sir Lindsay Parkinson for a civil engineering contract, also in August 1929, and then, after conversion to 3ft gauge, sent during December 1929 to the Castledearg & Victoria Bridge Tramway in Ireland. This locomotive was bought by the Hunslet Engine Co as it was still unsold at Stoke-on-Trent when they closed down in 1930. After being taken to the Hunslet works at Leeds it was overhauled and later sold for service overseas, via Robert Hudson Ltd, to Union Vale Sugar Estate, Mauritius, where it is possibly still at work. Hunslets supplied a new McLaren engine during 1945. Overall dimensions of the 60hp three-axle type were: length over frame 13ft 9in, height 9ft 1in, width over cab roof 6ft 9in, width over buffer beam 6ft, wheelbase 5ft 2in, wheel diameter 24in.

A total of eight of this type were built, varying slightly in weight to meet purchasers' and rail-gauge requirements and, apart from No 4415 mentioned above, were sold as follows: Robert Hudson sent Nos 4418/28 and 4432–4 to the Sudan Gezira Board during 1929 for use on the extensive cotton plantation 60cm-gauge railways; they are believed to be still at work today. Another Hudson sale was of No 4419 in 1928 to the 3ft 6in-gauge railway of the Roan Antelope Copper Mines, N'Dola. The most interesting sale was of locomotives Nos 4430/1 to the Central Railway of Ecuador in December 1929. These 75cm-gauge units were arranged as an articulated unit, coupled cab to cab, but could work independently if required.

Of the smaller 30hp two-axle version, it appears that only four were built, numbered 4465–7 and 4470 in the Kerr Stuart works list. Robert Hudson delivered No 4465 of 2ft gauge during May 1930 to the St Aubin Sugar Estate, Mauritius. No 4466 of 60cm gauge was built for Asiatic Petroleum Ltd and shipped to Shanghai, while No 4467 was given an 'exhibition finish' and sent to an exhibition of civil engineers' and contractors' plant at Scarborough in July 1930. It afterwards went to Joseph Boam Ltd, Middleton Towers, for use on the 2ft-gauge quarry line in part exchange for a 20hp 2½ ton Simplex locomotive. Edmund Nutall & Sons Ltd of Trafford Park took No 4470 for trial use on a contract on Shap Fell in Westmorland, the purchase resting on a three-month period, the result of which is not certain; it was of 2ft gauge. A further batch of works Nos 4471–7 and 4482 were also allocated but it is doubtful if any of these were built, although the first two were ordered. Overall dimensions were: length over frame 12ft 1in, height 9ft 1in, width over cab roof 6ft 9in, width over

buffer beams 6ft, wheelbase 3ft 6in, wheel diameter 24in.

An order for four of the largest locomotives in the Kerr Stuart narrow-gauge range was placed in April 1930 by Robert Hudson. This was for four 2ft 6in-gauge 90hp three-axle locomotives and though there is some mystery as to whom they were originally delivered it is known that they were shipped to South Africa and were in operation with Associated Manganese Mines of South Africa Ltd by 1936, as shown by an order for spares subsequently received by the Hunslet Engine Co. Carrying works Nos 4473–6, and weighing 15 tons, they had 7hp JAP petrol-starting engines and Ingersoll-Rand air compressors and reservoirs for operating wagon air brakes. The standard Kerr Stuart mechanical chain-drive transmission was fitted. At least two of these units were still at work in 1965.

A simple contractors'-type locomotive, known initially as type DX-1, was also built by Kerr Stuarts for general use on narrow-gauge lines. The first examples incorporated the Robertson patent transmission, which was an automatic variable-speed gear change unit, using the opposed diameters of two friction plates of different sizes and their movement across each other, to obtain different speeds to suit the loads being hauled, speed of operation, and gradients being climbed. Locomotive Nos 4422/6/7 had this gear fitted. After the Robertson gear, the transmission was to a countershaft by a train of helical gears and then through a reversing shaft and roller chain to the front axle, the two axles being coupled by a further roller chain.

Fig 46 *The 120hp twin unit 6w & 6WDM of 75cm gauge built in 1929 for the Central Railway of Ecuador by Kerr Stuart, KS 4430/1. The 60hp 6WDM and 30hp 4WDM were of the same design but single units were also built*

Fig 47 *Largest of the Kerr Stuart narrow-gauge diesels—four of 90hp for South Africa, KS 4473–6 (2ft 6in gauge)*

The first example, No 4422, was delivered in September 1929 to Boon's Granite Quarries near Nuneaton. Of 2ft 3½in gauge and named *Basset Green*, it was on trial for three months before being acquired over a twelve-month period on hire purchase. J. Arnold & Sons Ltd of Chipping Sodbury obtained the next example in August 1929 and bought it by monthly payments from November of that year. This locomotive, No 4426, was later purchased by Penlee Quarries Ltd of Penzance, and when it was scrapped in 1957 it was the last surviving example of its type. The Blackrock Quarries of Bryant & Langford Ltd took delivery of the final Robertson-fitted unit in August 1929. This was No 4427, and like No 4426, it was of 2ft gauge and was again purchased by monthly payments, being eventually acquired by Roads Reconstruction (1934) Ltd who used it at their Cranmore Quarry and scrapped it in 1957.

All were fitted with 30hp McLaren engines and soon had their Robertson transmission removed, as these had proved unsuccessful. The replacement transmission was unusual and incorporated a cone-type clutch; a rear-mounted two-speed gearbox was fitted and this was of the chain-reduction type, driving the transverse shaft by bevel drive. Chain drive led to the leading axle, both axles being chain-coupled. These locomotives weighed 4–5 tons in working order, depending on ballasting and rail gauge.

In view of the troubles experienced, a more conventional version of the same basic design was then built to a total of four units numbered 4429/60/1/8. Identical with the previous models except for type and layout of transmission, these all had cone-type clutches, a rear-mounted two-speed gearbox driving to a transverse shaft, and chain drive to the axles. No 4429 was built in 1929 for demonstration and was sent out on loan, including a period with Sir Lindsay Parkinson Ltd from October 1929 until February 1930. This 2ft-gauge unit was in due course sold, via Crown Agents, and shipped to

Fig 48 *The Kerr Stuart 30hp contractors' diesel. This example, KS 4429/29, seen in the maker's works, was supplied to Crown Agents at Haifa. The same design was used for the first Hunslet diesel in 1932 (2ft gauge)*

Haifa in March 1930. It was preceded by another example, No 4460, in November 1929, but unfortunately the purchasers are not identifiable from available records.

A 60cm-gauge example, No 4461, was shipped the same month to S. A. Ciments de Chalkis Portland Artificials at Piraeus, Greece, and the final example, No 4468, was delivered in April 1930 to Penlee Quarries Ltd, Newlyn, Penzance, being fitted with the engine from locomotive 4429, which received a new one prior to shipment. Dimensions varied slightly from locomotive to locomotive but No 4468 had an overall length of 9ft 3in, width of 4ft 10in, height of 7ft 6in, wheelbase of 3ft and wheels of 24in diameter.

Although during 1928-9 Hawthorn Leslie, and indeed Beyer Peacock, were supplying mechanical parts for English Electric electric locomotives, the Dick Kerr works of English Electric did build the mechanical portion of an obscure petrol-electric unit, supplied during 1929 to the Montreal Harbour Commissioners. This twin-bogie four-axle unit of 100hp was built for use as a service unit for the overhead electric system at the harbour, and fitted with crane, inspection platform and workshop, thus, possibly, being classed more as a rail inspection car than as a locomotive. It weighed 54 tons and was of standard gauge.

During 1929 Sir W. G. Armstrong Whitworth & Co Ltd of Scotswood-on-Tyne, Northumberland, built the mechanical parts of three large locomotives to the order of Sulzer Bros Ltd for use on the Buenos Aires Great Southern Railway in the Argen- tine (BAGSR) who were showing keen interest in diesel traction. These units comprised two diesel-electric mobile powerhouses and a diesel-hydraulic locomotive and were the outcome of an earlier proposal by Mr P. C. Saccaggio to try diesel power on the BAGSR, of which he was the chief mechanical engineer. The work was handled by the agents and consulting engineers, Livesey, Son & Henderson, who, together with Sulzer Bros, put the scheme in hand, giving Armstrong Whitworths the job of making the mechanical parts. The final erection and the installation of power equipment was carried out by the railway.

The powerhouses were interesting, in that they were fitted with a pair of 600hp Sulzer eight-cylinder-in-line engines operating at 700rpm, arranged side by side in the centre of the locomotive. Each engine drove its own Oerlikon generator and supplied current to two 144hp traction motors, giving two motors to each powerhouse. Each powerhouse was permanently coupled to its own five-coach suburban train set, the carriages of which had two four-wheel bogies each, one of each having a 125hp traction motor receiving current from the powerhouse. This meant that each powerhouse supplied current to twelve traction motors, six to each engine/generator set. The powerhouses themselves were of the all-over body type with a full width and length extending to the headstocks. A driving cab was provided at both ends and at the rear of the train set. The wheel arrangement was such that they had a rigid plate frame with the four axles, the outer two only being motored, and a pony

Fig 49 *The Armstrong Whitworth 1-C-1DH of 600hp for the* BAGSR *in 1929*
(5ft 6in gauge)

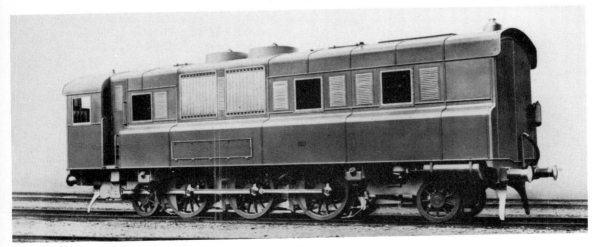

Fig 50 *The Perak River 'ship railway' 0–4–0PM of 125hp supplied in 1929 by Baguleys and the Drewry Car Co for service in Malaya,* BG *1696/29 (5ft 6in gauge)*

truck at each end. They were put to work on the suburban shuttle train service between Buenos Plaza Constituciòn station and Quilmes, working alternate days 16hr and 8hr duties seven days a week. These powerhouses, although soon obsolete in design, were still at work after World War II, having, of course, been re-engined. Main dimensions were: overall length 41ft, wheelbase 33ft, wheel diameter 37½in; weight in working order was 85 tons and top speed 46½mph. The train sets worked very well in service and paved the way for further experimental diesel traction in the Argentine.

The third locomotive was a heavy shunting unit, powered by a 600hp Sulzer engine similar to that of the powerhouses. The transmission was hydraulic, making use of an industrial-type Williams–Janney transmission of the swash-plate type, built for stationary and not traction use. Final drive was via a jackshaft at one end and side rods. This 76 ton locomotive was completely unsuccessful and never entered service, mainly because of the problems encountered as a result of excessive transmission oil temperatures and leakages. The transmission had a revolving swash-plate and variable stroke pistons and was arranged in two parts, rather like an engine and transmission in diesel-electric practice. The locomotive was 42ft in overall length, rigid wheelbase was 26ft 9in, driving-wheel diameter 4ft 7½in and maximum speed 28mph.

The Drewry Car Co Ltd's practice of selling Baguley-built locomotives through its London office under the Drewry nameplate ran into problems in 1929, and their association with Baguley (Engineers) Ltd became somewhat strained. It seems that this was partly due to some not too successful locomotives, and to an order for larger units which the

Baguley Shobnall Road works would have found difficulty in executing. The opportunity was, therefore, taken by Drewrys to seek another manufacturer, which turned out to be the English Electric Co, who agreed to do the work at their Dick Kerr works at Preston. Although Baguleys felt no immediate effect, the subsequent loss of Drewry's work, not to mention their well-established name and loss of the London sales office, was to bring difficult times to Shobnall Road.

Of special interest among the Baguley-built Drewry Car products of 1929 was the large 5ft 6in-gauge petrol locomotives of 0–4–0 type built for the Perak River Hydro-Electric Power Co Ltd for use on the Chenderch Ship Railway, Malaya. This locomotive, Baguley works No 1696, was fitted with rail clamps, a powered winch and special wet sanding gear, and was supplied with a boat-carrying wagon, 43ft long by 15ft wide, designed to carry two 10 ton timber rafts. The idea was that native boats, unable to navigate the river because of the construction of a dam, could be winched on to the wagon and conveyed by rail around the dam, before being refloated in the river. One of the largest petrol locomotives ever built, this 0–4–0 was powered by a 125hp Baguley six-cylinder engine and had a Baguley duplex clutch and three-speed transmission which gave speeds of 3, 6 and 10mph; final drive was by jackshaft and side rods. Weighing 18 tons in working order, the locomotive had an overall length of 17ft 8in, height of 10ft 1¼in, width 7ft 1in, wheelbase 7ft, wheel diameter of 30in. This machine last worked in November 1970 and lasted until early 1971, having survived the Japanese occupation of Malaya (not to mention the Malayan climate!), tribute indeed to Baguley workmanship.

Probably one of the most successful locomotive designs built at Shobnall Road was their first diesel locomotive, built in September 1929 for the Charnwood Granite Co Ltd, Bardon Hill, Leicestershire. This locomotive (BG 1699) was supplied by The Drewry Car Co and incorporated a centre cab with low bonnets at each side. The engine was a McLaren of 30hp with three cylinders. Transmission incorporated a cone-type clutch, and two-speed gearbox with bevel reverse. Final drive was by a jackshaft within the wheelbase and side rods. Weighing 6 tons, it had a 5ft 6in wheelbase and wheels of 20in diameter. Top speed was 7mph, and at 3·32mph the tractive effort was 2,200lb. The locomotive was withdrawn and sold for scrap but was fortunately purchased, re-engined and put to work at the Lougher Foundry of Ben Hughes Ltd in South Wales. It is still in existence, though out of use due to the discontinuance of rail traffic at the works—a worthy preservation item indeed.

In an attempt to fill some of the gap which would be left by the loss of Drewry's work, Baguleys took on general engineering work and essayed an entry into the miniature railway market. The latter product was based on the standard Baguley design with cylindrical water-cooling tank and it was a simple matter, by the addition of a chimney (which served as the engine exhaust), an imitation steam dome, mock side tanks and smoke-box door, to produce a fair resemblance to a steam locomotive, such being the popular demand! The first examples (BG 1695 and BG 1769) were supplied to the Lilleshall Estate Miniature Railway in 1928 and 1929, and were of 16hp and 25hp respectively. Others followed and were supplied to Lilleshall, and Wicksteed Park, Kettering. Rolling stock, too, was supplied and designs prepared for miniature steam locomotives and steam outline miniatures, including some for the projected North Bay Railway of Scarborough Corporation, though none was built.

The Avonside Engine Co introduced a standard range of petrol locomotives based on a centre-cab design with heavy outside plate frames regardless of rail gauge. Three examples were built, and the first, No 2013, was a standard-gauge unit with a Brotherhood–Ricardo four-cylinder paraffin engine set to produce 40hp at 1,000rpm, and starting on petrol. The transmission included a two-speed gearbox with a bevel drive to a transverse shaft with the final drive to both axles by roller chains. Speeds were 3·1 and 6mph. Main dimensions were: overall length 18ft 0¾in, height 10ft 4⅛in, width 7ft, wheelbase 5ft, wheel diameter 33in. This locomotive was supplied to E. S. & A. Robinson Ltd, Keynsham Paper Mills, near Bristol, and lasted until the late 1960s, though latterly as a spare locomotive.

The second of this type, No 2041, of 5ft 3in gauge, was delivered in 1929 to Union Cold Storage Co Ltd, Australia. In this unit a Dorman 4JOR four-cylinder petrol engine of 45hp at 1,000rpm was used. The transmission was similar to that of No 2013, as were the dimensions and speed range. Weight in working order was 9½ tons.

The largest and final example was the 5ft 6in-gauge unit built in 1931 for the North Western Railway of India, works No 2053/31, becoming their No 50 and employed on service duty in the

Fig 51 *A typical Baguley (Engineers) Ltd 'miniature' of 2ft gauge for the Alton Towers line in 1929, BG 1769/29*

Fig 52 *One of the standard Avonside centre-cab petrol shunters, in this instance one supplied to E. S. & A. Robinson Ltd, Keynsham Paper Mills,* AE *2013/32*

Stores Department. A four-cylinder Dorman type 4JORX engine was installed, rated at 53hp at 1,000 rpm, or 65hp at 1,450rpm, running on petrol. Transmission was identical with that of locomotives 2013 and 2041, and weight in working order was 12¾ tons. Dimensions were: length 20ft 1¾in over buffers, height 10ft 5in, width 8ft 3in, wheelbase 7ft 6in, wheel diameter 36in. At 3mph, tractive effort was 4,960lb and at 6mph, 2,460lb.

The first standard-gauge shunter by Kerr Stuart was a three-axle unit which, rather surprisingly, was delivered in December 1929 to Narrow Gauge Railways of Ravenglass, Cumberland, who operated the Ravenglass & Eskdale 15in-gauge railway and stone quarries at Murthwaite. The locomotive (KS 4421) was a diesel unit powered by a 90hp McLaren six-cylinder engine and had the usual chain-drive

transmission favoured by Kerr Stuarts, with the final-drive gearbox situated at the front of the locomotive; a two-cylinder petrol-starting engine was fitted. Weighing 18 tons 11cwt in working order, its main overall dimensions were: length over buffer beams 19ft 1¾in, height 10ft 6¼in, width 8ft, wheelbase 7ft 6in, wheel diameter 37in.

The locomotive worked over the mixed standard- and 15in-gauge line, linking the quarries with the mainline of the LMSR over which trains of wagons were worked. The locomotive worked as such until, upon the closure of the quarries, it was sold in 1953 to the dealers, R. Fraser & Co of Hebburn, who later resold it to the National Coal Board. It was used at Wingate Grange Colliery and rebuilt for the Coal Board in 1960 at Stafford by W. G. Bagnall Ltd, who fitted a 90hp Dorman engine but

Fig 53 KS *4421/29, a 90hp 6WDM built for the Ravenglass & Eskdale Railway, but shown here after modification by Bagnalls at the NCB Wingate Grange Colliery, Co Durham, in 1963. It is now with Rom River Reinforcement Ltd at Lichfield*

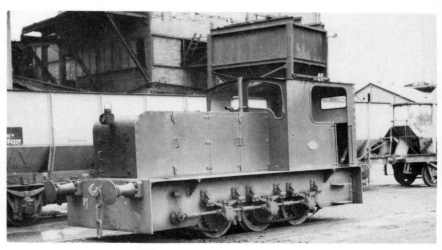

retained the original transmission. The external appearance was altered only slightly by fitting large front cab windows. The machine, now at Lichfield, is the property of Rom River Reinforcement Co Ltd, who bought it in 1968. It is hoped that, eventually, it will be saved for permanent preservation.

By 1930 Baguley (Engineers) Ltd were still in business at Burton-on-Trent and still making, by a special agreement, the smaller Drewry products such as inspection trolleys, cars and locomotives (especially 'one off' orders), the larger products and orders being executed by the English Electric Co Ltd at Preston. Baguleys also built a small number of Planet locomotives for F. C. Hibberd & Co, who were at that time without a subcontractor to build their locomotives. These enterprising moves, together with the successful miniature railway projects, were not, however, enough to save the firm, whose works were mortgaged in December 1930. Some of the last locomotives they built (for Wagon Repairs Ltd) were very simple standard-gauge machines, using standard railway wagon parts, transverse engines and chain drive, the first of a number of this type built later by E. E. Baguley Ltd. They had 25hp Ford engines and a Baguley two-speed gearbox based on Ford designs, giving 3 and 5mph. They carried works Nos 2071/2.

In August 1931 a receiver was appointed and the works closed down, the equipment being sold in November. In late 1932 the works was sold to Sharp Brothers & Knight Ltd, timber merchants.

The Planet narrow-gauge type built by Baguley (Engineers) was in the 1ft 6in–3ft 6in-gauge range, weighing 2–4 tons. The transverse engine layout was used, incorporating two engines of Ford manufacture, the 15hp and the 25hp, both with four cylinders. The transmission was a two-speed gearbox, giving 4 and 7mph; sliding dog speed-change gears of constant mesh type were fitted. Roller chains drove to both axles from the gearbox. Main dimensions were: overall length 8ft 4in, height 5ft 1in without cab, width 4ft 7in, wheelbase 3ft 6in, wheel diameter 13in or 17½in. Something like a dozen of these Ford Planets were built at Burton-on-Trent, plus, it seems, at least one standard-gauge Planet in the form of a 40hp 8 ton transverse-engined unit.

The smallest of the products of John Fowler & Co (Leeds) Ltd was the 1929 two-axle petrol locomotive which was first seen at the British Industries Fair in February 1929. This very simple unit, built no doubt to compete with Simplex locomotives, was essentially a flat-topped, steel-channel underframe, with a combined 10hp petrol engine and transmission placed centrally in the transverse position, with chain drive to both axles. The locomotive could haul 38 tons on level track and 12 tons on a 1 in 50 gradient, but very few were built.

CHAPTER 7

1930-1935: THE COMING OF THE LARGE LOCOMOTIVE

HUDSWELL Clarke & Co Ltd of Leeds, who since 1925 had been building small internal-combustion locomotives with petrol and diesel engines mainly for contractors' narrow-gauge lines, produced their first large unit in 1930. Ordered in 1929, it was delivered in March 1930 for the Junin Railway, or Compania des Litres if Ferrocarril de Junin, a 2ft 6in-gauge nitrate railway near Iquique, in Chile. It entered service in June and was employed on marshalling work and hauling trains of up to 50 tons weight up 1 in 33 gradients. The line closed and the locomotive was in use elsewhere by 1933.

This 32½ ton 1–C–1 diesel mechanical unit was reputed by its makers to have been the first application to a diesel locomotive of the Vulcan–Sinclair fluid coupling. The engine was a six-cylinder McLaren–Benz developing 330hp at 1,000rpm. It had a Bostock & Bramley four-speed gearbox giving speeds of 5·95, 8·8, 12·4 and 19·8mph, driving to a final drive and jackshaft unit at the front of the locomotive, with final drive by side rods. It had a rigid wheelbase of 7ft, overall wheelbase of 20ft and driving wheels of 33in diameter with pony truck wheels of 24in diameter. It carried works No D557 in the Hudswell Clarke list.

About this time, too, Hudswell Clarke were proposing what was virtually a diesel mechanical 'Garratt' articulated design. This design used two rigid-framed bogies with jackshaft and side rod drive and a centre frame unit pivoted to these in the Garratt fashion and carrying the power unit and driver's cab. The transmission from the engine was to be by flexible shafts from the gearbox to the final drive units located on each bogie. An artist's impression of a 2–6–6–2DM appeared in the technical press but, unfortunately, none was ever built.

Another firm which built its first, and in this case only, line service diesel locomotive during 1930 was D. Wickham & Co Ltd of Ware. This unit was for the Central Argentine Railway for branch line work and was of 5ft 6in gauge. It had two axles and an overall body, and was powered by a 90hp McLaren–Benz six-cylinder engine. A Wickham transmission incorporated an air-operated dry multiple-plate clutch, four-speed gearbox, of Wickham design but made by David Brown Ltd, giving speeds of 5, 10, 15 and 20mph. The final drive was through Simms Jurid couplings to a worm and wheel reduction box on both axles. The main engine was started by a two-cylinder petrol engine. Weight in working order was 18½ tons, overall length 20ft 6in, height 12ft 6in, width 10ft 2in, wheelbase 9ft, wheel diameter 37in. The locomotive remained the sole example and is believed to have worked well for many years.

The continued sale of reconditioned, modified or rebuilt Motor Rail Simplex locomotives of World War I vintage continued throughout the 1920s and into the 1930s. Reconditioned examples were sold, in some cases unaltered except for details. Modified ones often received new engines of makes not usually fitted to Simplex locomotives, this applying especially to the F. C. Hibberd examples. The rebuilding took various forms depending on the type of locomotive and who rebuilt them. The 60cm-gauge armoured Simplex locomotive type was rebuilt in various ways by altering the rail gauge, in some cases up to standard gauge, and by fitting new superstructures and cabs. The latter conversions were fitted with standard-height buffing and draw gear. This work was carried out by F. C. Hibberd and the results sold under the Planet nameplate, and also by Motor Rail, providing some interesting variations to complicate the scene.

Avonsides had built a number of double-bogie steam locomotives and closely followed them by a double-bogie diesel design of which only one example was built. This was Avonside No 2046

Fig 54 *The large
2ft 6in-gauge Huds-
well Clarke 1–C–1DM
for the Junin Rail-
way in Chile, 1930,
HC D557/30*

Fig 55 *A branch line
locomotive for the
Central Argentine
Railway of 90hp by
D. Wickham & Co
Ltd in 1930 (5ft 6in
gauge)*

Fig 56 *A standard-
gauge rebuild of an
ex-WDLR 60cm gauge
Simplex of 40hp by
Hibberds and sold
under the Planet
nameplate*

Fig 57 *The 1930 Ellingham Estate bogie diesel of 57hp by Avonside and thought to be possibly still at work in Natal, AE 2046/30 (2ft gauge)*

of 2ft gauge for Crookes Ellingham Estates Railway in Natal, this being Avonside's first diesel locomotive. Described as type DAW, the Avonside patent articulated locomotive employed a full-length main frame of rolled sections carrying the engine, transmission, water and fuel tanks, cab, etc, with a recessed or underhung section in the centre in which the reverse gearbox was located. Final drive was by a cardan shaft to a worm-axle drive-unit mounted on the outer axle of each bogie, both axles being connected by side rods. The drawgear was mounted on the bogies and an arrangement employed using intermediate drawbars to transmit the stresses of haulage to the central underhung section of the main frame containing a rigid dragbox. The drawbars were connected to the bogies by articulated joints.

The engine was a six-cylinder Gardner-type 6L2 of 57hp at 1,000rpm or 68hp at 1,200rpm. The three-speed gearbox gave speeds of 3, $5\frac{1}{2}$ and 8mph with tractive efforts of 5,350, 2,920 and 2,000lb. Weight in working order was 10 tons 9cwt, length over buffer beams 18ft 6in, between bogie centres 12ft, wheelbase of bogie 3ft, wheel diameter 24in, total wheelbase 15ft. This unit is thought to be still in existence.

John Fowler & Co (Leeds) Ltd built their first diesel locomotive in 1930 for the Chesterfield Tube Co Ltd. This 0–4–0DM (JF 18620/30) followed the standard Fowler design, hitherto used on their petrol-, alcohol- and paraffin-engined units, with jackshaft drive, end cab and tall chimney. This example was of 16 tons weight and 70hp and proved very successful in service. It was put to work in April 1930 and at the end of October 1932

its total cost in maintenance was just over £46, including wages and spares. The locomotive worked six days each week shunting in the works sidings with a 1 in 22 connection to the main railway line. It ended its days with International Combustion Ltd at Derby, and was scrapped in 1958.

The introduction in the late 1920s of a very simple and basic light contractors' locomotive by R. A. Lister & Co Ltd of Dursley, Gloucestershire, cannot go without mention. This locomotive used the power unit of the famous 'Lister Auto-truck', a rubber-tyred three-wheel vehicle commonly seen in GPO use at railway terminals. Sales of this locomotive, the 'Lister Rail Truck', had run into some hundreds by 1940 and production continued with little design alteration until late 1970.

This simple but very robust design was available in rail gauges from 16in to 3ft 6in and comprised an underframe, built up from rolled-steel sections of channel substantially cleated and gusseted, with added cross members and supports to carry the power unit which was bolted or riveted together to form a rigid structure. Cast-iron adhesion weights and buffing gear were fitted at each end.

The engine was mounted above the leading axle and was available in two sizes and power outputs. These were the 4–6hp type 'R' single-cylinder engine and the 9·8hp type 'RT' twin-cylinder engine, both of JAP (J. A. Prestwich) manufacture. The transmission, which was set in the centre of the locomotive frame, included a manually operated multiple-disc clutch to a Lister two-speed gearbox, giving speeds of $2\frac{1}{2}$ and 5mph for type 'R', and 3 and 6mph for type 'RT'. Chains drove to each axle from the gearbox secondary shaft.

The locomotives were in the 1–2 ton range, and weight could be varied to comply with rail gauges and customers' requirements. Typical 2ft-gauge examples had the following leading dimensions: type 'R' (type 'RT' where different is in brackets): length over frame 6ft 6in, length over buffing gear 7ft 5½in (8ft 7½in), width over axle box covers 3ft 1in, height without cab or canopy 3ft 8¼in (3ft 9¼in), wheelbase 2ft 6in, wheel diameter 12in. Curves down to 20ft radius were negotiable running light but to 30ft with a train.

The locomotives were supplied with an engine bonnet but cabs or canopies were not standard fitments. In due course Listers produced their own engines but the Rail Truck was not available in diesel form until the late 1950s. These units found use in a variety of industries all over the world and were always well liked as haulage units, despite, as was usually the case, little or no protection from the elements for the driver.

William Beardmore & Co Ltd, Glasgow, an old established firm who were known as builders of some of the finest steam locomotives and rail traction diesel engines in the world, built their first diesel-engined locomotives in 1930. This order, carried out in association with the General Electric Co Ltd (GEC) was for two 5ft 6in gauge Bo-Bo diesel-electrics for the North Western Railway of India. Delivery was made in June of that year, the locomotives costing £11,298 each.

These units were branch-line locomotives intended for working intensive branch-line shuttle services and were each powered by a six-cylinder Beardmore engine of 350hp at 900rpm. The GEC electrics included a main generator and four 85hp axle-hung traction motors. They weighed 48 tons

in working order with overall dimensions as follows: length over buffers 35ft 10in, overall height 12ft 9in, width 9ft, bogie wheelbase 7ft 8in, total wheelbase 23ft, wheel diameter 36in. Designed for a top speed of 55mph, maximum starting tractive effort was 29,176lb, and they were expected to handle a 100 ton load at 47mph.

The mechanical design was straightforward with overall body and driving cab at each end and they were rather similar to a Beardmore-engined locomotive-cum-baggage unit which was put to work in 1929 on the Buenos Aires Great Southern Railway. The locomotives were given trials in Scotland on an LMSR branch line prior to being sent to India.

The locomotives proved extremely troublesome, with flashovers on the traction motors at speeds of 36–42mph, and were incapable of being run at any higher speed. Some replacement motors of 89hp were fitted and, though not entirely satisfactory, were retained. The generators, too, gave trouble (failures of a serious nature occurring five times) as did the engines, but apart from a fractured crankcase nothing else too serious occurred. They entered service in February 1932 as Nos 330 and 331 and in a two-year period worked only eight months in traffic before needing heavy repairs and reconditioning. They re-entered service in mid-1936 with further short periods in traffic in 1937, 1938, 1939 and 1940, when they were finally withdrawn for scrapping. Respective mileages were 90,500 and 73,000. When running, they were cheaper to operate than equivalent steam locomotives used on the same services.

When Kerr Stuart and Co Ltd went into liquidation in 1930, it put an end to the good work they

Fig 58 *One of the two very unsuccessful* GEC–*Beardmore Bo-Bo diesel-electrics of 1930 for the North Western Railway of India (5ft 6in gauge)*

had been doing on diesel rail traction development, as well as to the first diesel road lorry which was about to go into production. However, all was not lost, for the business, designs and patents were purchased by the Hunslet Engine Co Ltd, who thereby gained the necessary know-how and a foothold in diesel traction. Hunslets took over two prototype locomotives and brought them to their Leeds works; these were the 60hp narrow-gauge unit (KS 4415/28) and the standard-gauge demonstration two-axle unit of 1929, Kerr Stuart No 4428.

The locomotives were carefully examined by Hunslets who, as we have already seen, subsequently sold the narrow-gauge unit but decided that some modification was needed on the larger machine. This was powered by a 90hp McLaren six-cylinder engine and the usual Kerr Stuart chain-drive transmission, rather similar to the three-axle Ravenglass & Eskdale locomotive. It had a length over buffer beams of 17ft 7¾in, overall height of 10ft 1¾in, width 8ft, wheelbase 5ft 5in, wheel diameter 3ft. Weight was 12½ tons in working order, and it had two speeds, 4·5 and 9mph.

Although it had been hired out by Kerr Stuarts to Gibbs & Canning Ltd between December 1929 and May 1930, it had serious transmission shortcomings which Hunslets set out to rectify. The manual clutch was replaced by an improved multiple-plate dry clutch and a new gearbox of Hunslet design of constant mesh type operated by compressed air, and the whole control system was revised.

After modification and tests, its new owners sent it out on hire to the Air Ministry at Cranwell during early 1932 with a new works plate reading 'Hunslet Engine Co Ltd', but retaining its Kerr Stuart works number. It was finally sold during September of that year to Eastwoods Flettons Ltd, Kempston Hardwicke Brickworks, where it remained, little used latterly, until it was acquired by the London Railway Preservation Society and installed at their depot at Quainton Road station, Buckinghamshire.

The first diesel locomotive to enter service with a British mainline railway was a diminutive machine of 18in gauge built by Hudswell Clarke and supplied in December 1930 to the Crewe Works Tramway of the LMSR. This 0–4–0 DM, works No D563, had a McLaren–Benz two-cylinder engine of 20hp at 800rpm. Its transmission included a multiple-disc clutch, a Bostock & Bramley gearbox, with a driven shaft driving a worm-reduction gearbox, and jackshaft and side rod final drive. Upon closure of the Crewe

Tramway it went to the Horwich works, where it remained until 1957 when it was scrapped upon the arrival of a new diesel locomotive.

Another Hudswell Clarke product which appeared in 1931 was their steam outline miniature railway diesel locomotive, supplied in small numbers up to 1938. The design was based loosely on the LNER Gresley Pacific tender locomotive and the first two examples were supplied to the Scarborough Corporation North Bay Railway, which operated just under a mile of 1ft 8in gauge. These two locomotives were *Neptune* (HC D565/31) and *Triton* (HC D573/32). Other examples of this type were No 4472 *Mary Louise* (HC D578/33), which was supplied to the 1ft 9in-gauge Blackpool Pleasure Beach Railway, and HC D582/33, supplied to Golden Acre Park, Leeds, 1ft 8in gauge, and which later went to Blackpool and then to Morecambe.

An LMSR Stanier Princess Royal version named *Carol Jean II* (HC D586/35) was built and supplied to Blackpool Pleasure Beach, and also two (HC D611 and D612) of 1938 for the 1ft 9in-gauge system at the Empire Exhibition at Glasgow. These were named *Princess Elizabeth* and *Princess Margaret Rose* and were both latterly with Butlins at their holiday camps at Pwllheli and Minehead.

Also supplied was a freelance design 4–6–4 side tank of which only two were built. The first (HC D570/32) was for Golden Acre Park, Leeds, later sent to Blackpool and then Morecambe, and the second (HC D579/33), named *Carol Jean*, to Blackpool.

All these locomotives had Dorman diesel engines of between 20 and 32hp located within the firebox. All had Vickers–Coates torque convertors and so were diesel-hydraulics. The Scarborough locomotives (HC D565/31 and HC D573/32) had 26hp Dorman two-cylinder engines running at 1,200rpm, transmission being by the Vickers–Coates convertor with worm-axle drive. The locomotive weighed 7½ tons and the tender 2½ tons; overall length was 24ft, width 4ft, height 5ft 6in, driving wheel diameter 28in, bogie and tender wheels 14in. They had a top speed of 20mph and were named (1931) *Neptune*, (1932) *Triton*.

The Baltic tank types had identical power and transmission equipment. They weighed 8 tons, and overall dimensions were: length 18ft 3in, height 6ft, width 4ft, driving wheel diameter 28in, bogie wheels 14in.

The Westleigh Stone & Lime Co Ltd, Burlescombe, Devon, took delivery in 1931 of an Avonside 3ft-gauge diesel mechanical 0–4–0 (AE 2061/31).

Fitted with a two-cylinder Dorman engine of 35hp at 1,800rpm, it had an Avonside two-speed, 3 and 6mph transmission, drive being taken from the engine through the clutch to a gearbox and bevel drive unit mounted at the front end which drove a jackshaft between the frames. From this a chain drove the leading axle, both axles being rod coupled. The locomotive weighed 4¼ tons and had a wheelbase of 3ft 6in and 24in diameter wheels, maximum tractive effort being 2,400lb.

A second example (AE 2076/34) was supplied, which was similar, except that the final drive unit was located at the cab end of the locomotive and it had wheels of 20in diameter. Both locomotives were scrapped in 1954 after a period of disuse.

The year 1932 was quite a busy year in the British diesel traction field, for not only were new large designs built but there were also some interesting developments among the locomotive manufacturers themselves.

Following the liquidation of Baguley (Engineers) Ltd and the sale of their Shobnall Road works, Major Ernest E. Baguley and a number of local businessmen founded a new company with a small works in Clarence Street, Burton-on-Trent, under the name of E. E. Baguley Ltd, Engineers. At first some orders left over from Shobnall Road were finished, spares taken over and supplied for previously built equipment, and a certain amount of repair work carried out. Later, as orders for new locomotives began to come in, it was evident that more space was required, so an adjacent plot of land was used and new works facing onto Uxbridge Street were built and opened in 1934. Production of the Baguley petrol engine, which had ceased upon the closure of the Shobnall Road works, was not resumed owing to the rapidly increasing popularity of the compression-ignition engine. Instead proprietary engines were used with the Baguley transmission, which was still being fitted in some orders until the early 1940s.

John Fowler & Co Ltd were still fully engaged in exporting their internal-combustion locomotives to many countries and during 1931 supplied one of the few British-built diesel locomotives to work in Russia. This unit, of conventional Fowler type, was adapted to operate under Arctic conditions and was an 0–4–0 DM of 45hp, built to the Russian standard railway gauge of 5ft.

New ranges of small contractors' locomotives appeared with some regularity during the early 1930s, the ubiquitous Ruston & Hornsby range being noteworthy among them. These locomotives, of simple yet substantial construction, proved an immediate success. The whole range was highly standardised and, apart from the earlier and smaller models, were fitted with Ruston diesel engines and Ruston gearboxes and mechanical chain-drive transmissions. The power range covered 10–50hp, all narrow gauge, all with two axles, and all with heavy underframes which could be ballasted with weights to suit differing haulage requirements. The range was continually being revised and updated, but without departure from the basic design concept. Later the whole range was fitted with Ruston-built engines. Designs were produced for gauges up to and over standard gauge, at first with 48 and 88hp models using two axles and chain drive, then in later years up to 400hp, using by the end of World War II electric and, later, hydraulic transmissions.

A typical 10hp narrow-gauge Ruston of 1932 had a Lister two-cylinder vertical engine and a Ruston three-speed constant-mesh gearbox, with

Fig 59 *One of the first two Hudswell Clarke 'steam outline' miniature railway Pacifics for Scarborough Corporation in 1931–2 both of which are still at work (1ft 9in gauge)*

Fig 60 *One of the many Ruston & Hornsby contractors' narrow-gauge diesels, in this case a 20–8hp model of the 1930s. A number of these have been preserved*

chain drive to both axles. Weight range was from $2\frac{3}{4}$ tons, length over frames 9ft $1\frac{1}{4}$in, width 3ft 3in, height without cab 4ft 11in, wheelbase 2ft $7\frac{1}{2}$in, wheel diameter 13in. The speed range was $2\frac{1}{2}$, 4 and 7mph.

In 1933 the 20–28hp version followed on after the original 10, 16, 20hp models, being generally similar but dimensions and details are quoted for comparison. Weighing 4 tons, it was available for rail gauges from 1ft 8in to 3ft 6in, being powered by a three-cylinder vertical Ruston engine giving 22hp at 850rpm, built in association with R. A. Lister & Co Ltd at Lincoln by Ruston & Hornsby. The transmission included a flexible-disc coupling to a Ruston three-speed gearbox of constant-mesh type. The final drive was to both axles from sprockets on the gearbox output shaft. Main dimensions for the cabless version were: length over couplers 10ft 4in, height 5ft $1\frac{1}{2}$in, wheelbase 2ft 9in. The slow-speed model ran at $2\frac{3}{4}$, $4\frac{1}{4}$ and $6\frac{1}{2}$mph, while the medium-speed version ran at $3\frac{1}{4}$, $5\frac{1}{4}$ and 8mph.

The 48hp model, for further comparison, had a Ruston four-cylinder vertical engine and a three-speed gearbox and final drive to both axles by chains. The speed range was $3\frac{1}{2}$, $5\frac{1}{4}$ and 8mph. Weight was from $5\frac{1}{2}$ tons, length over buffers 11ft $3\frac{1}{2}$in, width 3ft $3\frac{1}{2}$in, height without cab 5ft $6\frac{7}{8}$in, with cab 6ft 8in, wheelbase 3ft $4\frac{3}{4}$in.

Ransomes & Rapier Ltd of Ipswich built in 1932 one standard-gauge diesel electric shunter for use at their works. This two-axle unit had a 60hp McLaren engine, a BTH generator and one 30hp BTH traction motor with chain drive to the axles. Weighing $15\frac{1}{2}$ tons the 'Biffer', as it was affectionately called, was a 'one off' job not offered for commercial sale and so is outside the scope of this work.

The Rapier contractors' locomotives are, how-

ever, a different story. These were all two-axle 2ft-gauge units of $2\frac{1}{4}$ tons weight, powered by 10–12hp Lister two-cylinder vertical diesel engines. They had a cone-type clutch and a two-speed gearbox with final drive by chains. Overall length was 8ft $7\frac{1}{2}$in, height with cab 11ft, width 4ft, wheelbase 2ft $7\frac{1}{2}$in, wheel diameter 16in. A 1934 modification was in the $2\frac{1}{2}$–4 tons range. This had a 20–26hp Ailsa–Craig diesel engine, a plate-type clutch, a two-speed gearbox giving a top speed of 5mph, and final drive by chains. Overall dimensions were: length over buffers 9ft 5in, height without cab 4ft 11in, width 3ft 6in, wheelbase 2ft $10\frac{1}{2}$in, wheel diameter 18in. They were in production until 1939.

Another design appeared from Muir-Hill, the 'Model A' locomotive. This was a 2ft-gauge diesel unit powered by a 25hp Ford Model A four-cylinder engine. A Muir-Hill transmission, including a three-speed constant mesh gearbox giving speeds of 2·3, 4·2 and 7·24mph, drove via a cardan shaft to a reverse box mounted in the locomotive frame, which drove a final drive unit with chains to the axles. Weighing from 2 tons 13cwt, it was 7ft $8\frac{1}{2}$in in length, height without cab 4ft 7in, width 3ft 8in, wheel diameter 18in.

The first fruit of the absorption of the Kerr Stuart locomotive business so far as diesel traction was concerned was the completion at Leeds by the Hunslet Engine Co Ltd of their first diesel locomotive. This locomotive, works No 1700, was delivered in March 1932, and was a copy of the Kerr Stuart DX1 type with a straight mechanical transmission. It was built for Robert Hudson & Co Ltd for Ciments de Chalks Portland Artificiels, near Athens, Greece, and was virtually a repeat order following the delivery of Kerr Stuart No 4461 to this same customer in 1929. The engine was a 30hp two-cylinder McLaren and the transmission comprised a disc and cone clutch and a two-speed gearbox, giving speeds of 6 and 12mph, driving to a transverse shaft with chain drive to the wheels. Weight in working order was 5 tons 2cwt and dimensions were: length over buffers 9ft 3in, width 4ft 10½in, height 7ft 6½in, wheelbase 2ft 11⅞in, wheel diameter 24in. Hunslet No 1701 was a similar locomotive but it was never sold, being dismantled and some parts reused in locomotive No 1763. The entry of Hunslets into the light diesel locomotive market soon resulted in a flood of such machines emerging from their Leeds works.

Another 1932 design of interest was that of the light narrow-gauge transverse-engined units by Hunslet Engine Co Ltd. These were mainly sold via Robert Hudson Ltd who, between September and December 1932, sent one batch carrying Hunslet works Nos 1710–15 for use on a land reclamation scheme at Mucking in East Sussex. Another example (HE 1706) was delivered in June 1933 for service at Rye, Sussex, being repurchased by Hunslets in June 1938 and subsequently resold to Williamson Cliff Ltd of Stamford, Lincs, who did not scrap it until 1970, the last survivor of its type in the United Kingdom. These 2ft-gauge locomotives weighed 4 tons and had 20hp Lister engines driving via a plate clutch to a Hunslet three-speed gearbox, giving speeds of 2⅓, 4⅔ and 7mph; final drive was by roller chains to each axle. Overall dimensions were: length 7ft 2¼in, height without cab 5ft 8¾in, width 5ft 4½in, wheelbase 3ft, wheel diameter 18in. The design was very similar in appearance to the Fowler design of 1929.

Having at last become reconciled to the need of their own facilities for locomotive building, F. C. Hibberd & Co Ltd built and opened a works at Park Royal, London, in 1932. Since the closure of Kent Construction & Engineering Co Ltd at Ashford, the original Planet locomotive builders, and the takeover of the business from Honeywill Brothers, various subcontractors had been building Planet products. The problems caused by this system were many. The first of the subcontractors was Stableford & Co Ltd, railway wagon builders of Coalville, Leicestershire, who went out of business in 1928. The Bedford Crane makers, Bedford Engineering Co Ltd, then took over, until they, too, failed in 1930. Baguley (Engineers) Ltd built Planet locomotives during 1930 and it was when they were unable to continue that the Park Royal works was decided upon. Concurrent with the opening of the new works, the Hibberd range was widened to include the Howard locomotive range, which had been purchased from the liquidators following the failure of J. & F. Howard Ltd in 1931, and, it was this extended range of proven Howard designs which later provided the main production of the Planet business. Previously the majority of Planet locomotives, both narrow and standard gauge, had had transverse engine and transmission mountings, whereas the Howard range always used longitudinally set engines and transmissions. The Howard types were only very slightly modified when built at Park Royal.

Typical examples of these Planet–'Howards' were the 20hp petrol or diesel units of 4 tons weight. This type, retaining the open-box-type frame, was

Fig 61 *A Ransomes & Rapier 20–6hp contractors' diesel design of 1934. One example has been preserved (2ft gauge)*

Fig 62 *The Hunslet transverse-engined light contractors' diesel of the 1930s, HE 1706/32 (2ft gauge)*

Fig 63 *In 1932 Avonside supplied two of these 57hp 0–4–0*DM *shunters to the Penmaenmawr & Welsh Granite Co. At least one is thought to be still in use by a railway contractor,* AE *2062/3 of 1932*

similar to the Howard type 'H' locomotive. Overall dimensions were: length 9ft 10in, height over cab 5ft, width 3ft 6in, wheelbase 3ft 3in, wheel diameter 17¾in.

An example of the modified 10–12 ton Planet–'Howard' was the unit supplied in the mid-1930s to G. A. Harvey & Co Ltd, London. This locomotive with improved cab, works No 1981, ended its days at the Cleckheaton works of Yorkshire Tar Distillers Ltd. The box-type frame employed is prominent and was still in use after the end of World War II. The Planet range continued to include the transverse-engined types and also the reconditioned bow-framed Simplex 20hp type, plus derivatives of their own building.

The largest diesel locomotives built by the Avonside Engine Co were two standard-gauge machines supplied in 1932 to the Penmaenmawr & Welsh Granite Co Ltd, Penmaenmawr, North Wales. These two locomotives, Avonside works Nos 2062/3, were named *Kimberley* and *Attic* by the owners. Of the 0–4–0DM type, they were powered by a six-cylinder Gardner engine of 57hp at 1,000rpm or 74hp at 1,300rpm. The transmission was of Avonside design and incorporated a plate-type clutch with a three-speed gearbox giving speeds of 2, 5 and 9½mph. Final drive was taken from the gearbox under the cab by a cardan shaft to a worm-drive unit located on the leading axle, both axles being coupled by side rods. Weight in working order was 12½ tons, and overall dimensions were: length over buffer beams 15ft 6in, width 7ft 3in, wheelbase 5ft, wheel diameter 33½in. These locomotives could each haul a load of 415 tons on level track in low gear.

The design was very robust and when progressive abandonment of the Penmaenmawr rail system began both units were resold in 1968 for use with E. L. Pitt Ltd of Brackley. They were subsequently employed by Pittrail Ltd to lift many closed branch lines of BR and the NCB, and are possibly still so employed.

Avonsides designed a very similar locomotive of 100hp but none was built.

The delivery during 1932 of a batch of three diesel-electric shunting locomotives from the British Thomson-Houston Co Ltd to the Ford Motor Co Ltd, Dagenham, was noteworthy in that they were built by Metropolitan-Vickers at their Attercliffe works, Sheffield, to BTH designs, a practice common to the British industry when main contractors without facilities to manufacture their own mechanical portions received locomotive orders. These units were a radical departure in shunting locomotive design. Apart from the 1920 Hawthorn Leslie Paragon unit, albeit built only for trials, double-bogie shunting locomotives in British industry were unknown and even today are limited to a few examples, although their popularity seems likely to increase.

These Bo–Bo units were well designed, having cabs at both ends with access from open-end platforms, and a central power equipment compartment. The engine was an Allen six-cylinder in-line diesel unit of 150hp at 550rpm, one of the few rail traction applications of the excellent W. H. Allen engine. The engine drove a BTH main generator which supplied power to four 26hp BTH axle-hung, nose-suspended traction motors. Weighing 44 tons, these units had a maximum speed of 35mph and overall dimensions as follows: length 38ft 5¾in, height 13ft 3in, width 8ft 9in, bogie wheelbase 7ft, total wheelbase 25ft, bogie centres spacing 18ft, wheel diameter 38in. Maximum tractive effort was 24,000lb, and maximum axle load 11 tons. Air reservoirs were fitted for operating air-operated dumping cars. Their work included arduous steel works shunting and after a long and very successful working life they were replaced by new diesels in 1968. Thankfully, one is now preserved in Kent on the Kent & East Sussex Railway Preservation Scheme line, having been lent by GEC (Traction) Ltd.

The opening in 1931 of the Diesel Traction Department of Sir W. G. Armstrong Whitworth & Co Ltd, Scotswood-on-Tyne, was a very important milestone in the history of British diesel traction. The department was set up in the works, which had been on steam work since 1919, with full facilities for the production of Sulzer and Saurer diesel engines, for which licences had been obtained. The electric transmission system was chosen and the equipment manufactured to Armstrong Whitworth requirements by either Laurence Scot & Electromotors Ltd, Crompton Parkinson Ltd, Allen West Ltd or the English Electric Co Ltd. Some early orders, though, did have imported Brown-Boveri electrical equipment. Deliveries of diesel-electric vehicles began in 1932 with three 250hp railcars for demonstration on British mainline railways, the first of many railcars, railbuses and trainsets which were to form the bulk of the work of the Diesel Traction Department. These being outside the scope of this coverage, we shall concentrate on locomotives, shunters and powerhouses.

The first locomotives built were two demonstration diesel-electric shunters. The very first, an 0–6–0 of 40 tons, had an Armstrong–Sulzer six-cylinder 250hp engine running at 775rpm. The main generator by Laurence Scot supplied current to one force-ventilated, single-reduction type frame-mounted traction motor (also by Laurence Scot) set within the wheelbase over a final drive jackshaft unit with rod drive to the wheels. The maximum axle loading was 13 tons 2cwt and overall dimensions were: length over buffers 29ft, height 12ft 3in, width 8ft 6in, wheelbase 13ft, wheel diameter 42in, maximum tractive effort being 24,000lb.

This machine, which was the ancestor of the ubiquitous 350–400hp shunter of today, and was built under order DT7, carried works No D8 of 1932 and was sent out on trials on 11 July 1932. On the LNER it shunted and trip-worked at Forth Yard, Blaydon Yard and Heaton Yard for eighty-seven days. In a sixteen weeks' period the locomotive was scheduled to be on duty for 2,233 hours and actually worked 2,193 hours with engine hours at 1,505. A 98·5 per cent availability record was achieved, the only troubles being with brakes and a derailment. Engine availability was 100 per cent.

The locomotive was tried on the Southern Railway for fifty-eight days, working at Bricklayers Arms, Eastleigh, and Norwood Junction. Industrial service trials took place on the Hartley Main Colliery Railway in Northumberland, at Lever Bros, Port Sunlight, and at Preston Docks with Ribble Navigation for a total of fifty-seven days, the locomotive being finally purchased by Ribble Navigation in March 1935. During its trial period, it was in service for 202 days, working 4,579 hours with

Fig 64 *One of the three 1932* BTH *150hp Bo-Bo* DE *shunters for the Ford Motor Co, Dagenham. One is now preserved on the Kent & East Sussex Railway Preservation Scheme line*

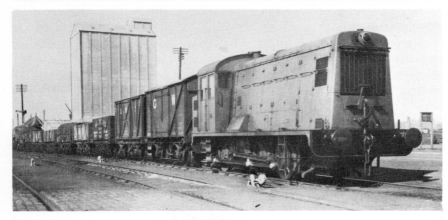

Fig 65 *Armstrong Whitworth's proto-type 1932 0–6–0*DE *of 250hp at work on Preston Docks, to whom it was eventually sold to survive until 1969,* AW D*8/32. A second example was built in 1934 for the* LMSR

Fig 66 *The 15-ton 95hp 0–4–0*DE *prototype by Arm-strong Whitworth in 1932. It remained as works shunter at Scotswood until it was scrapped in 1957,* AW D*10/32*

Fig 67 *One of three Hawthorn Leslie 2ft-gauge 0–4–0*DM *units for the Tokar-Trinkitat Light Railway in Sudan,* HL *3808/9 of 1933 and 3835 of 1934*

locomotive hours of 4,000½. This unit, carrying the name *Princess*, was scrapped at Preston in 1969 when new diesel locomotives were obtained.

The second shunter, works No D10, order No DT11, was a much smaller unit of 15 tons. It was an 0–4–0 type, and very different in concept from the 40 ton unit. Power was provided by an Armstrong–Saurer-type BLD six-cylinder engine of 95hp at 2,000rpm. This, together with its Laurence Scot generator, was set transversely across the locomotive frame at the front. Alongside this, approximately in the centre of the locomotive, was a Laurence Scot traction motor and a frame-mounted jackshaft-drive unit within the wheelbase, with rod drive to the wheels.

It began service in Scotswood works yard in December 1932 and worked there for three months before being sent out on demonstration to Appleby Frodingham Steel Works, Scunthorpe, Lyons Ltd, Greenford, North Eastern Electric Supply Co Ltd, Dunston-on-Tyne, and on passenger and goods service on the North Sunderland Light Railway, where its top speed of 27mph was found to be useful. During its first five months of service on the NSLR the locomotive covered 6,000 miles with trains composed of one or two passenger carriages plus one or two goods wagons, and although the line comprised only 4¼ miles between Seahouses on the coast and Chathill on the LNER main line, its weekly mileage averaged some 280 miles, using 66gal of fuel oil. The heaviest train worked was 90 tons but up to 200 tons shunting duties were easily undertaken.

Its length over buffers was 20ft, wheelbase 6ft 3in, wheel diameter 33in, maximum tractive effort 8,150lb. The driving controls were so arranged that they could be handled from the shunting platform along each side of the locomotive, making it unnecessary to enter the cab. The 'Mangle', as it was affectionately known, returned to Scotswood for yard work in August 1934 and remained the sole example of its design until finally scrapped in 1957.

During February 1933 Hawthorn Leslie delivered two small 0–4–0 diesel mechanical locomotives for use in hauling the annual cotton crop on the 20-mile long 2ft-gauge Tokar–Trinkitat Light Railway of the Sudan Railways, who gave them running Nos 55/56. They were of quite straightforward design, weighing 9½ tons and powered by McLaren six-cylinder engines, giving 100hp at 835rpm. A JAP twin-cylinder petrol-starting engine was fitted. The power was transmitted via a David Brown multiple-plate clutch to a three-speed Hawthorn Leslie gearbox, giving speeds of 3·3, 6·6 and 10mph. The final

drive, also of Hawthorn Leslie design, incorporated a worm-reduction gear drive of David Brown make, combined with a jackshaft and side-rod drive to the wheels. Here it might be recalled that Hawthorn Leslie's were one of the very first locomotive builders to employ worm-reduction gear for railway applications in their designs.

A further example (HL 3835) was built in December 1934, numbered Sudan Railways No 57, while the first two were works Nos 3808/9. Weight in working order was 9 tons, length over couplers was 16ft 10⅝in, height 10ft, width 5ft 6in, wheelbase 5ft, wheel diameter 28in.

The first standard-gauge diesel locomotive from Hunslet Engine Co Ltd (HE 1697/32) was put into service in March 1933, and owed much to the foresight of John Alcock, managing director of the Jack Lane works, Leeds, who saw that the company's future lay not with steam but with the diesel locomotive. This Hunslet unit was a typical three-axle machine intended for shunting duties and was noteworthy for being fitted with a German-made MAN diesel engine—a six-cylinder unit producing 150hp at 900rpm, and a maximum of 165hp at 1,000rpm. The transmission was the first of the familiar Hunslet units, incorporating a multiple-disc dry clutch, Hunslet patent constant mesh four-speed, oil-pressure-operated gearbox with manual reverse. Final drive was by jackshaft and side rods—a noteworthy departure from Kerr Stuart's established practice—and weight in working order was 21·4 tons. Main overall dimensions were: length over buffer beams 19ft 8in, width 8ft 2in, height 11ft 4⅝in, wheelbase 8ft, wheel diameter 42in. A two-cylinder 1,100cc JAP petrol engine was fitted for starting purposes. Built for demonstration purposes, the locomotive was almost immediately sent out on loan to the LMSR, with results we shall see later.

The Great Western Railway purchased its first diesel locomotive in April 1933 in the form of a standard Fowler 0–4–0DM. Painted in full GWR livery and carrying No 1 in the internal combustion series, it was obtained, after a period of demonstration with various firms, under Swindon order LOT No 289.

This locomotive (JF 19451/33) had a 70hp MAN six-cylinder engine, a multiple-plate clutch, four-speed gearbox and jackshaft and side rod final drive. Weighing 19½ tons it had speeds of 3, 6, 10·2 and 15mph and a tractive effort of 7,000lb at 3mph. Overall dimensions were: length 19ft 1in, height 10ft, width 7ft 1in, wheelbase 5ft 6in, wheel diameter 36in. After being employed mainly on departmental duties at Swindon, it was sold in March

Fig 68 *Hunslet Engine Co's first standard-gauge diesel, which was subsequently sold to the* LMSR. *This 150hp 0–6–0DM is still at work on the Middleton Railway at Leeds,* HE 1697/32

1940 to George Cohen & Sons of Leeds, who resold it to the Ministry of Supply later that year.

At long last, delivery began of the order placed with Drewry Car Co Ltd and, reputedly, one of the reasons for the Drewry–Baguley parting of 1929–30, since the units were too large for Shobnall Road to build. These units were not really locomotives but railcar-baggage units capable of hauling a train, either singly or in pairs, over the standard-gauge Bermuda Railway system. Built at the Dick Kerr works of English Electric, they were twin-bogie units having a full-length body with central baggage compartment, powered by two 150hp Parsons M8 petrol engines. The transmission was of the Wilson preselective five-speed epicyclic gearbox type, driving by cardan shafts to the wheels. This was the first application of this transmission to rail use and makes these units worthy of mention here. The engine and transmissions were mounted on the bogies. Some trial runs were carried out on the LMSR from Preston to Longridge.

To some extent following the example of Armstrong Whitworth, the Belfast firm of Harland & Wolff Ltd made an effort to gain a foothold in the growing diesel rail-traction field. Unlike Armstrong Whitworths, they had had no previous locomotive building experience, but both firms were heavy engineers, with shipbuilding as their main activity. They also had other similarities in common. Like the Scotswood-based firm, Harland & Wolff took out a manufacturing licence for a continental engine, used mainly electric transmissions, and were manufacturers for a similar period of time.

Harland & Wolff used the Burmeister & Wain

Fig 69 GWR *No 1— a typical Fowler 70hp 0–4–0DM of 1933,* JF 19451/33

two-stroke diesel engine and, as we shall see later, built their first locomotive in 1933 as a shunting unit for the LMSR. Their first really interesting production during 1933, under order No 8252, was in the form of a 5ft 3in-gauge diesel-electric for the Belfast & County Down Railway (BCDR). Powered by a Harland B & W four-cylinder engine giving 270hp at 850rpm, it drove a Harland & Wolff main generator, which supplied current to two Laurence Scot nose-suspended, axle-hung, self-ventilated, traction motors located on the centre and rear axles, giving an axle arrangement of 1–Bo or, in steam parlance, 2–2–2–0!

Overall dimensions were: length 28ft 7½in, height 12ft 5¼in, width 8ft 11in, wheelbase 12ft, wheel diameter 43in. Weighing in working order 33·2 tons, it was a rigid-frame design with a top speed of 50mph. Built to the requirements of the railway's locomotive engineer, Mr J. L. Crosthwait, it had electric train-heating equipment and worked with complete success on the Ballynahinch branch. These duties included passenger services with shunting work, and required the capacity to haul 200 ton goods trains up 1 in 100 gradients at 16 mph. A typical day's work for this unit would have been not less than sixteen hours.

Numbered D1 by the railway, this locomotive was later passed on to the Ulster Transport Authority and sold back to its makers in 1951. It was finally scrapped in 1969.

Armstrong Whitworth's contribution during 1933 to locomotives and powerhouses was quite varied.

Of particular British interest was the prototype mainline Universal locomotive built under order No DT8 and carrying works No D9. Built for demonstration purposes, it employed a Scotswood-built Armstrong–Sulzer type 8LD28 engine. This eight-cylinder, in-line unit was set to give 800hp at 700rpm. A Laurence Scot generator supplied power to three axle-hung, self-ventilated, nose-suspended traction motors by Crompton Parkinson.

The mechanical portion comprised a plate frame-type underframe with the three driving axles set in the centre with pony trucks at each end, giving a 1–C–1 axle arrangement. It had an overall body with a driving cab at each end, and in addition, at one end, a small bonnet housing a transversely-mounted engine generator set, comprising an Armstrong–Saurer type 6BLD six-cylinder 75hp engine which supplied power to the various auxiliaries on the locomotive.

Capable of a maximum speed of 70mph, it weighed 74 tons in working order, of which 51 tons were adhesive, and maximum axle load was 17 tons. Overall dimensions were: length 39ft 10in, height 12ft 8in, width 9ft, total wheelbase 30ft, driving wheel diameter 48in.

After initial trials on the LNER in the North Eastern area, and following various adjustments, the locomotive went into service on the LNER on 19 February 1934. It was put to work on freight services between Newcastle and Berwick, Newcastle and York, Newcastle–Berwick–Tweedmouth, Berwick–York–Newcastle, and later on passenger work

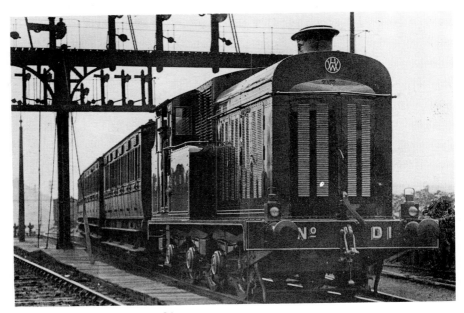

Fig 70 *For use on the Ballynahinch branch of the* B & CDR, *Harland & Wolff built this 270hp 1–Bo* DE *in 1933. Shown here on trial at Belfast Queen's Quay when new (5ft 3in gauge)*

Fig 71 *The 1933 prototype Universal mixed traffic 1–C–1* DE *by Armstrong Whitworth. Seen here in the maker's yard at Scotswood works,* AW D9/33

between Newcastle and Carlisle. Trial runs on empty passenger stock between Newcastle and Tweedmouth were also included. This locomotive covered over 26,000 miles, using 25,000gal of fuel before being taken out of service, never to return, due to engine failure, and was stored at Scotswood until it was dismantled in 1937.

Although, as with earlier attempts, this innovation was doomed to failure because neither the steam-minded engineers on the mainline railways, nor vested interests in the locomotive industry and petroleum refining industry, were in favour of diesel power, the advent of this type of locomotive did at least demonstrate its potential, especially when used in multiple. It would have been possible with a fleet of such units to work the majority of services, both freight and passenger, on any British mainline railway except perhaps the heaviest and fastest Anglo–Scottish expresses. The simplification of spares for such a standardised fleet would alone have produced great economies.

Other large units built at Scotswood were for the Buenos Aires Great Southern Railway (BAGSR) and were all of 1,700hp, and of 5ft 6in gauge. Order DT3 comprised three mobile powerhouses which were ordered in 1931 following the success of the two lower-powered 1929 units. These were twin units of Bo–2 + 2–Bo axle arrangement, being numbered UE3/4/5 by the railway company. Designed to operate with an eight-coach train set of motorised suburban trains, each unit was powered by two eight-cylinder Sulzer 8LV34 vee-type engines, rated at 850hp at 550rpm and giving a total horse-power of 1,700 per unit. The generators, by Brown-Boveri, supplied power to twenty English Electric axle-hung, nose-suspended traction motors. These motors were located so that each twin unit had four motors, with the remainder distributed on the train

sets at two per carriage and each engine/generator set supplying current to ten motors each. Weight in working order was 132 tons, overall length 65ft, height 13ft 9in, driving bogie wheelbase 8ft 4in, carrying bogie wheelbase 6ft 6in, wheel diameter $37\frac{1}{2}$in, and maximum speed 60mph, maximum tractive effort being 60,000lb.

These units were placed in service between 13 June and 31 July 1933 on the accelerated suburban service between Buenos Aires and San Vocente, two units being used, with the third as a spare. By the end of 1936 mileages were quoted as, UE3 251,121 miles, UE4 221,887 miles, and UE5 187,554 miles. Average running per year was 66,000 miles, the running cost being around 1s 0d per mile. The trains are believed to be still at work, though they have been re-engined.

The same power equipment was used for a twin-unit 1,700hp mainline locomotive completed under order DT4 in 1933. With the axle arrangement of 1A–Bo + Bo–1A this unit, numbered CM 210 by the BAGSR, entered service on 1 October 1933. Weighing 145 tons in working order and with a top speed of 90mph, it was 75ft $3\frac{1}{2}$in in overall length. The wheel diameters were: driving wheels 42in, carrying wheels $37\frac{1}{2}$in, the bogie wheelbase was 9ft. Maximum tractive effort was 63,500lb.

This locomotive was an unquestionable success, as can be gathered from the fact that by the end of October 1936, after just over three years' service, it had covered 197,171 miles with an average fuel consumption of 1·15mpg. The cost of fuel, lubricating oils, running and maintenance (excluding overheads and capital costs) was approximately 10d per mile.

After running-in on local services, it was put on the Bahia Blanca night express passenger service between Buenos Aires and Olavarria. This run of

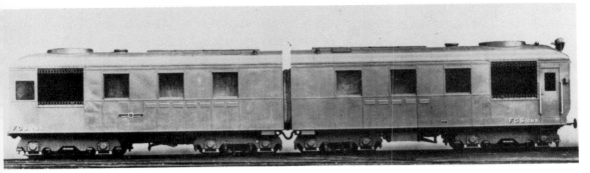

Fig 72 *One of the three Armstrong Whitworth 1,700hp mobile powerhouses for the* BAGSR *in 1933 (5ft 6in gauge)*

206 miles was done in 6–7hr (dependent on the number of stops en route) and often only 15min was left for turn-round before making the return run. Train weights were between 450 and 650 tons.

A test with a 3,150 ton freight train over a 106-mile route was carried out in 6hr. By 1943 the locomotive had run 798,822 miles with only fourteen total failures in traffic. Partial failures totalled twenty-eight, though none of these prevented the completion of the locomotive's trip.

Examples of the causes of complete failures were burnt-out traction motors, engines failing to start up, axlebox bearing failures; in some cases these were due to mishandling by crews or maintenance staff deficiencies. Probably the mechanical design was responsible for most of the troubles. The aluminium body panels which had been used to

keep the overall service weight down to the limit set for two-axle bogies, were not satisfactory, and there was a notable lack of any efficient systems for air-extraction or dust-free intake of air for cooling purposes.

The locomotive was, however, considered a good basis for further development and had it not been for World War II a twin unit design of 2,000hp might have been built as a successor to CM 210, which was still at work in the 1950s and may even be today.

By 1930 the European, Asian and American railways and railway industries were also making significant progress in the diesel locomotive field. In Germany work was commencing on high-speed diesel trains of railcar type, a lead soon followed by the USA. On the locomotive side, it was the Danish

Fig 73 *The highly successful Armstrong Whitworth 1,700hp 1A–Bo–Bo–A1*DE *locomotive of 1933 for the* BAGSR *(5ft 6in gauge)*

firm of Frichs who were perhaps leading. Their Siamese State Railway diesel electrics, the 1,000hp, and later in 1932 the 1,600hp locomotive, of twin-unit, twin-engine layout, are outstanding examples which enjoyed great success and longevity. These units included six of 1,000hp with 2–Do–2 axle arrangement, each with two 500hp Frichs engines, and one with two 800hp Frichs engines with 2–Do–Do–2 notation. All had Oerlikon electrical equipment. Also delivered were two similar 900hp units to Danish State Railways; these 2–Do–2 units lasted until after the war.

Sulzers also supplied six 450hp Henschel-built A1A–A1A diesel-electrics to Thailand in 1931, following closely on the heels of a 750hp Sulzer-powered shunter which had been delivered to Manchuria the previous year. In Germany, Krupps built a twin Sulzer-engined locomotive of 1,600hp weighing 149 tons. This 2–Eo–1 diesel-electric was put into service in Russia during 1932. Meanwhile Deutz had another attempt at a form of direct drive with their 2–B–2 unit of 1,500hp, built in 1933, and continued experimental work on it until 1938 but without success.

Algerian Railways, then part of the PLM Railway of France, took one Homecourt-built 2–Co–2 diesel-electric powered by a 920hp MAN vertical engine. This unit was not scrapped until 1958, after running for some years equipped with two 650hp Sulzer engines and was noteworthy as being one of the first express passenger diesel locomotives to be capable of up to 75mph with light trains.

Final pre-war developments included 4,400hp twin units with Sulzer engines for Romania and the Société Nationale de Chemins de Fer in France. These were of 2–Do–1 1–Do–2 notation (1938) and 2–Co–2 2–Co–2 (1937).

Hydraulic transmission was still not popular for large applications and there was some surprise at the appearance at the Nürnberg Railway Centenary Exhibition of 1935 of a Krauss–Maffei-built diesel-hydraulic of 1,500hp. This incorporated the largest Voith transmission so far applied, operating via a jackshaft and side-rod drive arrangement to the three-coupled axles of this 1–C–1 rigid-framed locomotive. It lasted until 1957.

Eventually, of course, hydraulic transmission in its various forms established itself, though not until some twenty-five years after its first successful applications by McEwan, Pratt & Co Ltd in England. Similarly, electrical transmission was generally adopted and has always remained more in favour than the hydraulic systems evolved later, especially for larger locomotives.

In 1933, Armstrong Whitworth put in hand order DT22 for six standard-gauge 15–17 ton diesel-electric shunters. These 0–4–0 units were numbered D21–D26 in the Armstrong Whitworth works list, and were built for demonstration in the hope that sales would quickly follow. Very different from the 1932 15 ton shunter, order DT11, these robustly constructed locomotives had a conventionally mounted engine generator set comprising a six-cylinder Armstrong–Saurer 6BLD engine developing 85hp at 1,700rpm. The main generator was by Laurence Scot, who also built the traction motor, which, as was customary in Armstrong Whitworth shunter designs, was frame mounted, with gear drive to a jackshaft-drive unit and side-rod drive. Overall dimensions were: length 19ft 4in, height 10ft 10in, width 8ft, wheelbase 5ft 6in, wheel diameter 36in.

Although extensive demonstrations were carried out with the locomotives, sales were slow and some units were not disposed of until after the closure of the Diesel Traction Department. The locomotives were demonstrated at Dunston Power Station; Dorman Long & Co Ltd, Middlesbrough; Warner & Co, Cargo Fleet, War Department, Shoeburyness; Gas Light & Coke Co Ltd at Beckton; the Admiralty, Chatham Dockyard; Bass-Worthington, Burton-on-Trent; Bede Metal & Chemical Co Ltd; ICI; Austin Motor Co Ltd; Dunlop Ltd; Nevills Dock Co Ltd. The locomotives were sold as follows: D21 to Dunston Power Station; D22 to A. Reyrolle & Co, Hebburn; D23 to the Admiralty, Chatham Dockyard; D24 to Dunlop Rubber Co Ltd; D25 to North Sunderland Railway; D26 to Magnesium Elektron Co Ltd. The locomotive supplied to North Eastern Electric Supply Co Ltd, Dunston, was operating at a cost of 19s 8½d per hour as against 28s 6d for steam traction. This unit, together with the one at Reyrolles, was still in use in 1970. Although the latter was subsequently laid aside pending possible sale, the Dunston locomotive is still at work. The Reyrolle unit was sold in late 1971 to W. F. & J. R. Shepherd of Byker, Newcastle upon Tyne, and is now working again.

During June 1933 W. G. Bagnall Ltd supplied what was to be the first of four similar locomotives built up to 1936 for the Ashanti Goldfields Corporation Ltd, Gold Coast. It was put to work in Ashanti over rough mining-type trackwork with gradients up to 1 in 25 and curves of 60ft radius, replacing a wood-burning steam locomotive. This 2ft-gauge design was carried on two two-axle bogies and powered by a six-cylinder Gardner diesel engine of 62hp at 1,100rpm. The transmission was a

Fig 74 *One of the six 15-ton 0–4–0DE shunters of 95hp built in 1933–4 by Armstrong Whitworth. The example shown is the one for Dunston Power Station, and is still at work,* AW D21/33

Bagnall design unit incorporating a two-speed and reverse epicyclic gearbox, Vulcan-Sinclair fluid coupling, and cardan shaft drive to worm-axle drive units on the first and fourth axles, with side-rod drive to the inner axles.

These locomotives had electric lighting and carried works Nos 2494/33, 2514/34, 2546/36, and 2568/36 which did not incorporate a fluid flywheel. They were shipped to Takoradi and ranged in price from £1,950 to £1,990. Overall dimensions were: weight 12 tons, length 20ft 6in, height 9ft, width 5ft, bogie wheelbase 3ft, total wheelbase 15ft, wheel diameter 20in. Tractive efforts were 5,350lb at 3½ mph and 1,900lb at 10mph.

By this time all the British mainline railways had in operation some form of internal-combustion

locomotive of either narrow- or standard-gauge types. They were mainly used for rather specialised requirements in the engineering departments and not for general service.

It was to the LMSR that the distinction of ordering this type of locomotive for general shunting use first fell. Shunting locomotive activities, it was found, were accounting for up to 50 per cent of the total freight locomotive hours on the railway by 1930 and various schemes were examined to see if some economy could be made by adopting alternative methods of traction for this work. Included in this survey was the Sentinel-geared steam locomotive also tried by the LNER and GWR, but it was the diesel locomotive which really attracted the LMSR's operating department, and

Fig 75 *In the period 1933–6 W. G. Bagnall built four twin-bogie diesels for Ashanti Goldfields Ltd. The one illustrated is* WB 2494/33 *(2ft gauge)*

orders were placed with outside contractors for locomotives of this type in 1932.

Prior to these orders the LMSR put into trial service an experimental unit numbered 1831. This unit was rebuilt at Derby works from the frames and running gear of an old Johnson 0–6–0T of Midland Railway, of 1870s vintage. Rebuilt during 1932 to form a 46-ton diesel-hydraulic shunting unit, it had an all-over body which housed a 400hp Davey–Paxman six-cylinder engine coupled to a Haslam & Newton transmission, driving to the wheels through a Scotch-Yoke final drive and side rods. The Haslam & Newton transmission was of the variable delivery pump type 'twin' transmission. Although meeting considerable difficulties initially, it was put into running stock in June 1934 and remained in use until 1939, when it was converted to a mobile generator unit. In this form, numbered MPU 3 (Mobile Power Unit), it spent its time in the Midlands during the Second World War as a standby generator set, and was noted out of use in a siding at Crewe South in mid-1951. Overall dimensions were: length 30ft 3¾in, height 12ft 8in, wheelbase 15ft 8in, wheel diameter 55in.

Orders placed by the LMS during 1932 with five different manufacturers were for nine locomotives, only one of which had electric transmission. Deliveries took place in 1933–4, but some units were not actually put into running stock until 1935. Nos 7400–08 were allocated, but only three actually carried them for they were soon renumbered in the 7050–58 series. All were three-axle units, except for No 7050, which had two axles.

Dealing with them in numerical order: No 7050 was the two-axle unit designed by the Drewry Car Co Ltd and built at the English Electric Company's Preston works. Carrying Drewry works No 2047, it was put into service in 1934 and had a 176hp W. H. Allen 8RS18 eight-cylinder in-line engine, and the now familiar Vulcan–Sinclair fluid coupling. It included also a Wilson four-speed epicyclic gearbox with jackshaft and side-rod final drive by Bostock & Bramley. The speed range was 2·9, 5·1, 8·5 and 12mph. Weight in working order was 26 tons, wheelbase 7ft, wheel diameter 36in, maximum tractive effort 11,200lb, top speed 12mph.

Before delivery, it was put on trial in Preston Docks early in May 1934 and found capable of handling trains of 400 tons weight, in addition to being able to fly shunt 200 ton trains. After operating mainly in Salford Goods Yard, it was sent on loan in 1940 to the War Department and eventually purchased by them in March 1943. It is believed

still in operation with the WD, although now with a 153hp Gardner 6L3 six-cylinder engine and a new Wilson–Drewry air-operated gearbox.

No 7051 was the Hunslet prototype unit of 1932 which was taken by the LMSR as the first of four units on order with that builder. Purchased in March 1933, it had undergone extensive trials in the Hunslet yard of the LMSR. At first numbered 7401, it was soon renumbered 7051 and lent to the WD during the war years, after which it was repurchased by its builders, who overhauled it and re-equipped it with a new 132hp McLaren 6MR engine. It was used as a hire locomotive and works shunter for some years until going, in August 1960, to the Middleton Railway Trust in Leeds. They now use it on their public freight service and, very fittingly, have named it *John Alcock*, after the man responsible for Hunslets entering diesel traction in 1932.

No 7052, originally 7402, was delivered by Hunslets in January 1934 carrying works No 1721 of 1933. It had a 150hp McLaren–Benz 8MDB eight-cylinder engine and an auxiliary Scott petrol engine for starting purposes. Transmission was similar to locomotive No 7051, with a multiple-disc dry clutch, Hunslet patent constant mesh two-speed gearbox with oil-pressure operated sliding dogs, and integral manual reverse to a final-drive jackshaft unit with side-rod drive.

Weight in working order was 26·4 tons; overall dimensions were: length over buffer beams 21ft 8½in, height 12ft 1in, width 8ft 3in, wheelbase 9ft, wheel diameter 40in, maximum tractive effort 12,800lb. At first on loan to the WD and later sold to the Admiralty in 1943, it spent most of its time at the Broughton Moor Armament Depot, Cumberland, until November 1966 when it was sold to Birds Commercial Motors Ltd, Long Marston, who scrapped it in 1969.

The third of the Hunslet units, LMSR 7053, was put into traffic in September 1934 and had a 150hp Brotherhood–Ricardo RZS six-cylinder engine, started by a petrol-driven air motor. The transmission included a Vulcan–Sinclair hydraulic coupling, a Humfrey–Sandberg free wheel, and a David Brown two-speed epicyclic gearbox with integral manual reverse gear. The free wheel and David Brown gearbox were later replaced by a Cotal four-speed gearbox with separate manual reverse. Final drive was by jackshaft and side rods. Weight in working order was 26·3 tons. Overall dimensions were: length over buffer beam 21ft 8¼in, height 12ft 0⅞in, width 8ft 3in, wheelbase 9ft, wheel diameter 40in. This unit (HE 1723/34) was sold to the WD in 1939, though not taken out of stock until December 1942, and was later resold to its makers with a view to rebuilding and resale. This, however, never took place and it was finally dismantled for scrap in 1954–5 at the Hunslet works.

The final Hunslet unit (HE 1724/34) was delivered in October 1934 as LMSR 7054. The heaviest of the Hunslet quartet at 29 tons, it had a 180hp Davey Paxman 6V25 six–cylinder engine with an auxiliary petrol-starting engine. The transmission comprised a Vulcan–Sinclair fluid coupling, Humfrey–Sandberg free wheel and a Hunslet patent three-speed gearbox with integral manual reverse and jackshaft and side-rod drive.

Sold to the WD after periods of loan in 1943, it was eventually repurchased by Hunslets, who reconditioned it and sold it for further use in collieries in Yorkshire. By 1955 it was at Brodsworth Main and in 1960 was rebuilt as a diesel hydraulic with a Rolls Royce engine by Hunslets. Overall dimensions were: length over buffer beams 21ft 8¼in, height 12ft 4⅞in, width 8ft 8in, wheelbase 9ft, wheel diameter 40in, maximum tractive effort 15,780lb.

Nos 7055/6 were the only two of the batch which were of identical design, being built by Hudswell, Clarke & Co Ltd (HC D580/34 and D581/35) and placed in traffic in 1935. Powered by 150hp Mirrlees–Ricardo eight-cylinder engines, they had a Vulcan–Sinclair coupling and a Bostock & Bramley three-speed gearbox with integral manual reverse. Drive was through a cardan shaft to an axle-mounted worm-axle drive unit and side rods.

These 30 ton locomotives had a short life as such, for 1939 saw them fitted to work as mobile generator sets and numbered MPU2 and MPU1 respectively. One of these, formerly LMSR 7055, was still in service on BR during the 1960s as a generator set. These units had a wheelbase of 9ft, 40in diameter wheels and a maximum tractive effort of 12,500lb.

The locomotive numbered 7057 was interesting in that it is the only example of this manufacturer's work to be used on a British railway (some were and still are at work in Northern Ireland). Built by Harland & Wolff at Belfast under order 2503, it was a 27·17-ton unit fitted with a 150hp Harland B & W TR4 four-cylinder two-stroke engine, which started by a petrol/paraffin air compressor. Transmission was via a Vulcan–Sinclair hydraulic coupling, and an SLM two-speed constant-mesh gearbox with manual reverse. Drive was via a cardan shaft to a Bostock & Bramley worm-axle drive unit on the leading axle; side rods coupled all axles. In 1935 a new SLM worm-drive axle unit was fitted. Length over buffers was 25ft 4½in, height 12ft, width 8ft 6in, wheelbase 12ft, wheel diameter 38in; maximum speed was 10mph and tractive effort 11,200lb. No 7057 was sold to the Northern Counties Committee in 1943 and rebuilt by Harland & Wolff with a 225hp engine and regauged to 5ft 3in, becoming eventually Ulster Transport Authority No 22. It was taken out of service in 1965.

The solitary diesel-electric, No 7408, was a Scotswood-built Armstrong Whitworth machine completed in 1933 under order No DT20, carrying works No D20, and was very similar to the 1932 unit subsequently purchased by Ribble Navigation

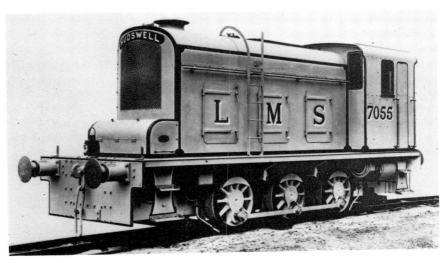

Fig 76 *The Hudswell Clarke 150hp 0–6–0*DM *shunters for the* LMSR *in 1934–5,* LMSR 7055/6, HC D580/1 *of 1934–5*

Fig 77 *Harland & Wolff 0–6–0*DM *of 150hp for the* LMSR *in 1933. It was subsequently sold to the* NCC *in 1943 and converted to 5ft 3in gauge*

Ltd, Preston Docks. The LMS unit differed in having larger fuel tanks and vacuum brake equipment.

The engine was the 250hp Armstrong–Sulzer six-cylinder unit, with a Laurence Scot generator and one frame-mounted Laurence Scot traction motor, having forced ventilation and single reduction gear drive mounted above a jackshaft final drive unit set within the wheelbase. Length over buffer beams was 25ft 6in, height 12ft 5¾in, width 8ft 6½in, wheelbase 13ft, wheel diameter 42in. Weighing 40 tons, it had a maximum axle load of 13½ tons, overall dimensions being as for the Preston locomotive.

It was put into service on the LMSR on 14 February 1934 as No 7408, quickly becoming No 7058, and operated at Brent, Crewe, Beeston, Toton and Bescot. Early reports proved this locomotive's success, as in one year it covered 9,200 miles, averaging over 22hr service each day, thus paving the way for the ubiquitous diesel-electric shunter of today. This unit was the only one of the nine shunters to enter BR stock upon nationalisation and was allocated running No 13000, though withdrawn without ever carrying it in December 1949. The records of these shunters proved the superiority of the diesel-electric for heavy use and the need for powers of 300hp for future units.

The Royal Arsenal Railway, Woolwich, took delivery of an 18in-gauge locomotive in February 1934, the first double-bogie diesel to be built by the Hunslet Engine Co Ltd. This locomotive (HE 1722/34) named *Albert*, was an end-cab design of conventional appearance, powered by a McLaren–Benz MDB4 four-cylinder engine of 75hp at 1,000

rpm, with a short-period rating of 82hp at 1,100 rpm. The transmission was a Hunslet patent plate clutch which drove via a Hardy Spicer shaft to the main gearbox mounted in the centre of the locomotive frame between the bogies, with Hunslet preselective gears and speeds of 4 and 8mph. Shafts drove from both sides of this main gearbox to worm-reduction boxes mounted at the outer end of each bogie. These drove jackshafts which in turn drove the wheels by side rods, all shafts having universal couplings.

Starting was by a 16–19hp Scott petrol engine. Weight in working order was 13¼ tons, overall length 18ft 1⅛in, height 9ft, width 5ft 1½in, bogie wheelbase 3ft, total wheelbase 12ft, wheel diameter 20in. It could negotiate 30ft radius curves and had a maximum tractive effort of 6,570lb. This interesting locomotive was unfortunately sold for scrap in October 1961 to R. N. Bradbury Ltd of Warrington.

After taking out a licence with the German locomotive builders, Deutz, W. G. Bagnall Ltd commenced production at their Stafford works of the standard Deutz shunting locomotive range. The first productions were for mining use. Bagnall No 2498 was built in March 1934 for Halkyn District United Mines Ltd, Bryn Owel, Flintshire. This was a twin-bogie four-axle unit of ungainly appearance, 1ft 10½in gauge, powered by a two-cylinder Bagnall–Deutz engine of 24hp at 700rpm and weighing 6½ tons. The engine, as was the case with all Deutz engines used by Bagnalls, was imported from Germany as Bagnalls did not themselves build Deutz engines at Stafford. The transmission included a two-speed epicyclic gearbox driving by

Fig 78 Albert, *the 75hp Hunslet 18in-gauge bogie diesel for Woolwich Arsenal*, HE 1722/34

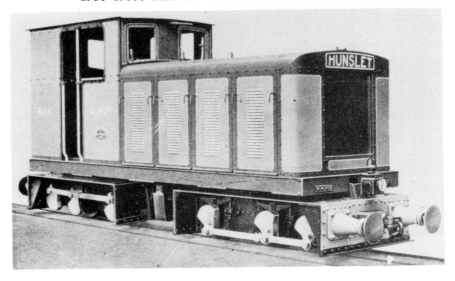

cardan shafts to the inner axles of each bogie via a worm-axle drive unit, side rods coupling the axles together. Electric lighting was fitted and the locomotive cost £1,300. The unit had a short life and was scrapped in 1937.

The second unit (WGB 2499/34) was a more conventional mining locomotive of pure Deutz design and 1ft 11⅝in gauge. Delivered in March 1934 to Oakley Slate Quarries Ltd, Blaenau Festiniog, this locomotive was transferred to the nearby Votty & Bowydd Quarry, who scrapped it in 1963.

Power was provided by a Deutz single-cylinder horizontal engine giving 8·5hp at 1,200rpm, which was hand-started. A Bagnall-built welded gearbox of two-speed type was fitted, driving via chains to the wheels. Weight in working order was 2·8 tons. No exhaust conditioner was fitted and the loco-

motive cost £298. Maximum tractive effort was 1,190lb.

A second example (WGB 2524/35) was delivered in January 1935 to New Consolidated Goldfields Ltd, South Africa.

Two examples of another Deutz type were built and delivered, the first in May 1934 and the second in May 1938. They were 4–4½ ton 2ft 6in-gauge units with 12–24hp two-cylinder engines, and four-speed gearboxes. These were Bagnall Nos 2506 and 2595 and were supplied to Budla Beta Tea Co Ltd, Assam. Overall dimensions of these locomotives were as follows: length over buffers 10ft 2in, height 7ft 8½in, width 3ft 10in, wheelbase 3ft 0⅝in, wheel diameter 16in. Maximum tractive effort was 1,980lb.

Two large 0–4–0DM shunters of metre gauge were built by Bagnalls for Assam Railways &

Fig 79 *Two Bagnall–Deutz diesels, a 12–24hp 2ft 6in 0–4–0DM for the Budla Beta Tea Co of Assam—* WB 2506/34, *and a 55hp metre-gauge 0–4–0DM for Assam Railways & Trading Co,* WB 2507/34

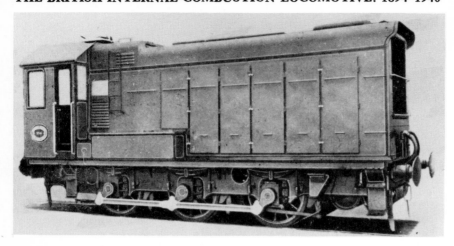

Fig 80 *The prototype English Electric 0-6-0DE of 300hp built in 1934 by Hawthorn Leslie and subsequently purchased by the LMSR, HL 3816/34. A further ten were purchased by the LMSR in 1935–6*

Trading Co Ltd in 1934/5. Fitted with Deutz engines, they were WGB 2507/34 of 55hp, delivered in May 1934 and weighing 11½ tons. Both had a Deutz four-speed gearbox and Bagnall final drive with jackshaft drive and main dimensions were: overall length 13ft 7¼in, height 9ft 2in, width 6ft 10½in, wheelbase 4ft 7½in, wheel diameter 27½in.

The 1935 example (WGB 2530/35) was a larger 79hp unit weighing 14 tons and was delivered in September of that year. It had a Deutz four-speed gearbox, giving speeds of 3·25, 5·15, 8·15 and 13mph; again jackshaft and side rod drive was employed. Overall dimensions were: length 16ft 6in, height 9ft 2in, width 7ft 2½in, wheelbase 4ft 7⅛in, wheel diameter 27½in.

Concurrent with the LMSR shunter deliveries, the appearance of the first English Electric diesel electric shunter from the Hawthorn Leslie works at Newcastle on Tyne caused great interest in the British diesel traction field and, for reasons to be discussed later, probably made the greatest impact on British mainline railways in so far as shunting duties were concerned.

Built as a demonstration locomotive, this unit (HL 3816/34) was placed in service in April 1934. The engine was the now famous English Electric type 6K, built at the English Electric Willans works at Rugby. This large six-cylinder in-line engine was set in this application to operate at 300hp at 650rpm.

The electrics were by English Electric and comprised a main generator and two 150hp nose-suspended, axle-hung, self-ventilated tractor motors with single-reduction gear drive mounted on the two outer axles.

The mechanical portion, of Hawthorn Leslie build, was a simple design based on three axles

and proved, by virtue of its continuance throughout a production life of twenty-nine years for this type of locomotive, to have been very sound in concept. Overall dimensions were: length 28ft 6in, height 12ft 4in, width 8ft 9in, wheelbase 11ft 6in, wheel diameter 48½in, weight in working order 51 tons 7cwt, with a top speed of 35mph and a maximum tractive effort of 30,000lb.

The LMSR tried this locomotive extensively during 1934–5 generally on 24hr service for 6½ days each week, using it for heavy shunting at Crewe, Rugby, Salford, Beeston and Camden yards. Examples of typical weeks of service may be noted. At Crewe during the week ending 28 April 1934 it covered 178 miles, being on duty for 109 hours with a total engine hours of 99, and using 2·5gal of fuel for each engine hour. At Camden yard, week ending 14 July 1934, it ran 225 miles and was on duty 151 hours, out of which engine running hours were 126, the fuel consumption being 2·52gal/hr.

So successful was this unit that it was decided to order ten of the same design, together with another ten to an enlarged design from Armstrong Whitworths based on LMSR 7058 of 1933. The ten ordered, which were of Hawthorn Leslie–English Electric manufacture, differed only in detail from the prototype, which was finally purchased by the LMSR, modified with larger fuel tanks and shunting steps at Crewe works, and taken into stock as LMSR No 7079 in December 1936. This machine became 12002 in BR stock and was finally withdrawn in June 1956.

Another Hawthorn Leslie product of 1934 was that of the 0–6–DM for the Air Ministry at Cranwell, where it was employed over the 6-mile line connecting the depot with the LNER.

Delivered in September, this unit (HL 3817/34)

was most interesting in that it employed the final engine development of Beardmores, a light six-cylinder unit of 200hp running at 1,100rpm. The transmission was a Hawthorn Leslie three-speed gearbox and final drive including a spur drive to a jackshaft final drive with coupling rods. A Humfrey–Sandberg clutch was fitted. It was numbered AMW & B No 135. Weight in working order was 27 tons, its speed range 4·7, 8·4 and 15mph and the wheelbase and wheel diameter 8ft 4in and 40in respectively. The mechanical design was conventional with an end-mounted cab and rear jackshaft drive unit.

A typical Fowler design using a simple straight mechanical drive and mechanical portion was built in 1934 for plantation work in Natal, being unusual in that it was of the 2–4–0 wheel arrangement. This 85hp Fowler–Sanders-engined unit weighed 17 tons, was for 2ft gauge and had a total wheelbase of 9ft 9in, and coupled wheelbase of 4ft 9in, with driving wheels of 28in diameter. Fuel capacity was 45gal. Similar 0–6–0 type units were built in 1935 for sugar plantation service in Queensland.

During 1934 E. E. Baguley Ltd opened their new works in Uxbridge Street, Burton-on-Trent, in which they concentrated on the production of new locomotives, generally using engines and transmissions bought in for the purpose, though in some cases, especially in the smaller products, Baguley transmissions were still used. Overall production embraced general engineering work, diesel locomotives carrying Baguley nameplates, and Drewry Car Co Ltd rail inspection vehicles. Output also included some small locomotive orders,

battery electric and electric locomotives for electrical manufacturers, mainly under subcontract, such as British Thomson–Houston Co Ltd (BTH), Metropolitan–Vickers Ltd, and the English Electric Co Ltd, a practice still pursued today by the company.

Production of the steam outline miniature locomotive was also continued and the four earlier Baguley (Engineers) units were followed by first rebuilding a fifth unsold example, (BG 1797), as BG 2083 for Trentham Gardens. This was followed later by 2085 and 3014 for Trentham with 40hp Baguley engines which had been in store, the latter unit being a 0–6–0. During 1939 a simplified derivative was produced without jackshaft drive, and one, BG 3024, was sold prior to the outbreak of war. This model was revived in post-war years, mainly for Butlin's Holiday camp miniature lines.

Armstrong Whitworth's Diesel Traction Department was busy in 1934 producing some interesting diesel-electric units of varied designs for a number of customers. Although not strictly locomotives, two of these productions are worthy of mention. These were 'half-locomotives' in that both comprised an articulated powered section, housing driving cab, engine and generator plus traction motors, and carried on two bogies, one of which carried, articulated to it, the passenger train set with which it worked. This arrangement was favoured by Armstrong Whitworths, and as the power units of the trains were separate, they perhaps merit coverage here.

The first to be completed under order DT19 was a three-coach train set with powerhouse for the

Fig 81 An 85hp Fowler 2–4–0DM for plantation service in Natal in 1934 (2ft gauge)

5ft 6in São Paulo Railway in 1934. The powerhouse carried an Armstrong–Sulzer 6LD 25 six-cylinder engine developing 450hp at 700rpm, though derated to 382hp. This drove a Laurence Scot main generator and supplied electricity to four Crompton Parkinson traction motors, located in pairs on the axles of the leading bogie of the powerhouse and the last bogie of the train set. A 50hp Armstrong–Saurer engine/generator set was provided for auxiliaries.

The powerhouse was built at Scotswood works and measured 25ft over body, with bogie wheelbase of 8ft. The driving wheels were 48in in diameter, while carrying, or non-powered, bogie wheels were 43in in diameter; top speed was 60 mph. The three passenger coaches were arranged so that the first was articulated to the powerhouse and the other two articulated together. A driving cab was provided in the rear carriage.

After initial trials between Santos and São Paulo, working two round trips per day, six days per week, this unit covered 1,036 miles per week, excluding 14 miles each trip up the rope-worked Sierra incline when the power was shut down. After short periods for modifications and overhauls, it worked over the same route, making two round trips on six days and one on Sundays and covering 1,115 miles a week. By 26 May 1935 it had covered 43,993 miles, and by 24 November 1935 this had risen to 64,268 miles. By October 1936, after working a service of three round trips a day, six days a week and two trips on Sundays, it had covered 139,590 miles in service. A report dated 9 March 1937 stated that during its first two years from 2 July 1934 no failures in traffic had occurred, except for some bogie suspension troubles. Thus, it was still in traffic for 602 days, the days out of service being mainly taken by routine maintenance and overhaul work.

A somewhat similar unit was supplied to the Buenos Aires Western Railway in September 1934 under order DT30. The same type of engine and electrical equipment was used and the powerhouse differed only in being articulated to the one coach of the train which had a driving compartment at its outer end. The only power bogie was the leading one of the powerhouse, which had two axle-hung traction motors. The rail gauge was 5ft 6in and the whole unit was 89ft 10in in overall length and capable of a top speed of 72mph. In its first 53 weeks' service the vehicle covered 120,000 miles prior to its first overhaul. Only nine days were lost owing to mechanical troubles and no trouble was experienced with engine or transmission during this period. By the end of 1936 it had covered 228,300 miles, only minimum difficulties having been experienced with its Sulzer engine, none of which resulted in failure.

The first British public railway to be completely operated by diesel traction was the North Sunderland Light Railway which ran between Chathill and Seahouses in Northumberland. This railway had previously provided test facilities for Armstrong Whitworth locomotive D10/32, and no doubt as a result of these trials they purchased in 1934 a modified 15 ton DT22 type shunter. This unit (AW D25/34) was a standard unit suitably modified by fitting a larger capacity generator to permit the locomotive to operate at higher speeds over long distances than it was capable of in its shunting form. This modification improved performance in the 15–20mph speed range and raised the maximum speed from 25mph to 30mph.

Mainline buffing and drawgear was fitted, and also a vacuum brake. The engine was a six-cylinder Armstrong–Saurer 6BLD-unit of 85hp at 1,700rpm. A Laurence Scot generator and frame-mounted traction motor were fitted, with jackshaft drive and side rods. Named *The Lady Armstrong*, it proved very successful working all types of traffic over the 4½-mile light railway, paying off its initial cost over steam in eighteen months and saving 5d per train mile, amounting to £330 per year.

A Manning Wardle steam locomotive was held in reserve but the North Sunderland Light Railway was probably the first public railway in the world to be 100 per cent dieselised! During the first five months, *The Lady Armstrong* covered 6,000 miles, resulting in a monthly mileage of around 1,460 being achieved by mid-1936, and an annual mileage of about 17,500.

A somewhat similar shunter was built by Armstrong Whitworths for the Ceylon Government Railways, who put it in service on 15 October 1934. It was employed on duties in the Ratmalana works yard, and was numbered in Ceylon stock as No 500. Built at Scotswood under order DT44, this 5ft 6in-gauge 0-4-0DE unit had a six-cylinder Armstrong–Saurer 6BXD engine developing 122hp at 1,400rpm. The generator and frame mounted traction motor were made by Laurence Scot and, as usual with this type of locomotive, final drive was by jackshaft and side rods.

Weighing 20 tons, it was 21ft in overall length, 11ft high, and 10ft 2in wide over cab roof. Wheelbase was 5ft 6in, and wheel diameter 36in. Its top speed was 20mph and its maximum tractive effort 12,000lb. Its working day was eight hours for five days each week and in 20½ months it had covered 8,175 miles at a cost of 8·41d per mile.

Another Armstrong Whitworth shunter of 1934 was the 2ft 6in-gauge 0–4–0DE machine for use on the railway operated by the St Kitts Basse Terre Sugar Factory, India. The engine was a six-cylinder Armstrong–Saurer type 6BLD of 85hp, but derated to 78hp at 1,700rpm in this application. The generator and traction motor were by Laurence Scot and the motor, which was frame-mounted, drove to the wheels via a cardan shaft, a worm-axle drive unit on leading axle, both axles being coupled by side rods.

Built under order DT36 it weighed 12 tons, was 16ft 2½in in overall length, height 10ft, width 6ft 6in, wheelbase 5ft 6in, wheel diameter 33in. Top speed was 25mph and maximum tractive effort 7,500lb. Designed for haulage service in the 3–12 mph range, it operated, however, at speeds up to 20mph in a tropical climate of 86°F in the shade with loads of sugar cane, hauling trains of up to 75 tons weight between the sugar cane fields and the factory. Shunting work in the harbour entailed loads of up to 100 tons and in the busy season it worked up to 20 hours each day.

Following the success of the Universal 800hp locomotive on its trials on the LNER, and after talks with representatives of the Indian State Railways (who were keen to try the diesel-electric traction system with a view to obtaining experience and some idea of its suitability for mainline work in India), Armstrong Whitworth put in hand two similar units for use in India.

Built to meet Indian requirements and of 5ft 6in gauge in anticipation of an order, two Universal-type locomotives of improved design were completed to Indian State Railways' loading gauge. These units, built under order No DT23 and carrying works Nos D27 and D28 of 1934, were 'proper' mixed traffic locomotives designed to work long-distance passenger or freight traffic in full tropical conditions of humidity and 120°F shade temperatures. Enough fuel for 1,000 mile runs was carried and the locomotives could be used either in multiple unit or singly, each unit having two driving cabs. In the event, however, and before their actual completion, the Indian order was for two 1,200hp locomotives, so the builders were left to complete the locomotives and search for a purchaser.

The engines fitted were eight-cylinder-in-line Armstrong–Sulzer 8LD28 producing in this application 800hp at 700rpm. The main generator, by Laurence Scot, supplied power to three Crompton Parkinson nose-suspended, axle-hung, force-venti-lated traction motors mounted on the three rigid axles of the locomotives 1–C–1 axle arrangement.

An auxiliary engine generator set with a 75hp Armstrong–Saurer six–cylinder engine was fitted and carried across the locomotive in the engine compartment, a different arrangement from the British prototype of 1933 which had the unit set across one end of the locomotive in front of the driving cab.

Weight in working order was 81 tons, of which 52½ tons were available for adhesion. Maximum axle load was 17·5 tons and a top speed of 70mph was attainable. A minimum curve of 5 chains was negotiable and the maximum tractive effort was 28,500lb. Overall dimensions were: length 43ft, height 13ft 6in, width 9ft 10¾in, total wheelbase 30ft, rigid wheelbase 14ft 3in, driving wheel diameter 48in, pony truck wheel diameter 36in.

After completion, arrangements were made with the Ceylon Government Railways to allow full-scale trials of the locomotives and the pair were shipped, hopefully, to Ceylon in early 1935 for a six months' period. Both were put into service in February of that year. Unit D27 was in service for 63 days, covering 18,291 miles with an average fuel consumption of 1·11mpg, but was put out of action when a traction motor failed with a broken banding wire. It was taken into the Ceylon Government Railway workshops for attention, but during lifting a crane chain broke, allowing the locomotive to fall 3ft 6in to the floor. Although it was first thought that damage was only slight—a bent axle and twisted items of framing—D27 returned to traffic after repairs only to fail again shortly afterwards with a broken crankshaft. Upon subsequent inspection, this was found to have been caused by its fall when the engine mounting had been put out of alignment.

Locomotive D28 continued at work until a cylinder block cracked on 29 May, by which time it had covered 16,036 miles using 1·19gal of fuel per mile in 55 days. The agreed six months' period being up, no more trials were permitted and no sale was made.

During operations, the locomotives worked between Colombo and Talaimanar, mostly on Indian mail trains of up to eighteen bogie carriages and weighing around 500 tons. Typical weekly rosters were: (A) 2,009 miles in 102 hours; (B) 2,432 miles in 118 hours. Costs of operation totalled 1s 0d per mile including all charges. The locomotives were capable of handling the trains single handed and did so at approximately half the cost of steam traction. In four months the pair

Fig 82 *The 800hp 1–C–1* DE *Universal locomotives by Armstrong Whitworth in 1935. These locos were demonstrated in Ceylon but not sold until 1937–8 to the* BAGSR, AW D28/9 *of 1935*
(5ft 6in gauge)

covered 34,237 miles. During the trials, the makers maintained the locomotives and were paid 75 per cent of steam mileage costs for the same mileage by the railway. The locomotives were returned to Scotswood for repairs and overhaul, and to await a purchaser.

The very extensive 75cm-gauge railway system in the Nile delta was still steam worked when Hunslets delivered their first diesel locomotive in October 1934. This 0–4–0DM unit of 11½ tons weight was powered by a 112hp McLaren six-cylinder engine running at 1,000rpm. It had a friction-type plate clutch and a Hunslet preselective air-operated three-speed gearbox giving 5, 10 and 20mph. The final drive was by a rear-mounted jackshaft and side rods. Designed for a top speed of 20mph, it had a maximum tractive effort of 7,850lb. This unit (HE 1740/34) had overall dimensions as follows: length 14ft 3in, height 11ft 1$\frac{3}{16}$in, width 7ft 4in, wheelbase 5ft 9in, wheel diameter 26¼in.

During 1935 Harland & Wolff built only one locomotive, this being a 3ft 6in gauge 0–6–0DM shunting unit, No 400, for the Sudan Government Railways. Following introduction of the narrow-gauge Hawthorn Leslie units, this railway wanted further experience of diesel traction and so acquired this unit and two others from English Electric for shunting duty. The former was fitted with a Harland B & W type TR4 four-cylinder two-stroke engine of 190hp running at 1,200rpm, driving via a Bostock & Bramley four-speed gearbox, giving 3·6, 6·4, 10·8 and 18mph. Final drive was by a

cardan shaft to a Bostock & Bramley worm-axle drive unit on the leading axle, all axles being side-rod coupled. During 1938 the unit was re-engined with a type TR6 six-cylinder engine giving 225hp at 1,200rpm and fitted with a new transmission, of similar type but incorporating a Vulcan–Sinclair hydraulic coupling.

Weight in working order was 31·45 tons and maximum tractive effort was 17,500lb. Overall dimensions were: length 25ft 1in, height 11ft, width 9ft, wheelbase 12ft, wheel diameter 39½in.

Another Bagnall–Deutz engined locomotive was the large 50hp mining locomotive delivered during January 1935 to the King's Hill Colliery of the Coltness Iron Co Ltd at Newmains, Scotland. This two-axle unit had a Bagnall four-speed gearbox to a Bagnall final jackshaft drive unit, weighed 8 tons and had flame-proofing fitted. This 2ft-gauge unit cost £1,275.

Although they built a few petrol-paraffin locomotives from around 1928, the firm of James C. Kay & Co Ltd, Phoenix Foundry, Bury, Lancashire, is not well known and details of its output are somewhat obscure. One of their final products and the last British survivor would seem to have been the 1ft 11$\frac{5}{8}$in-gauge unit delivered to the Knostropp Sewage Works, Leeds, in 1935. This example, one of the two basic models offered by Kays, who sold them as Premier locomotives, was scrapped early in 1966 after having been dismantled for some time pending overhaul.

The narrow-gauge model was built in gauges up to 1m and in the 2½–5 ton range. The Knostropp example weighed 4½ tons and was powered by a 35hp American Waukesha vee-type four-cylinder vertical in-line engine with Ricardo heads. Overall dimensions were: length 8ft 5in, height to top of silencer 4ft 11in, height with cab 7ft 6in, width 3ft 8in, wheelbase 2ft 11in, wheel diameter 18in. Two-speed gearboxes giving either 2½ or 3¾mph or 6½ and 9mph were fitted.

The larger model, designed for gauges from 1m to 5ft 6in, weighed up to 12 tons, the overall dimensions being: length 13ft 6in, height over cab 9ft, width 6ft 9in, wheelbase 5ft 6in, wheel diameter 33in. Again, two gearbox speed ranges were available, 1¾ and 4½mph or 2¼ and 5½mph. At 2mph the tractive effort was 6,300lb.

The mechanical portion was standard, being built up from rolled-steel channels filled in with cast-iron weight blocks, machined and bolted into the channels, with the possibility of additional blocks for ballast being fitted if required. A power winch or capstan take-off fitting could be provided at the rear, and the locomotives ran on tapered roller-bearing axleboxes.

The power equipment included proprietary engines, up to 45hp, and the Kay patent type transmission, designed by a Mr Caton, included a dry multiple-plate friction clutch and two-speed constant mesh gearbox. Final drive was effected by twin roller chains to the leading axle, both axles being coupled by a further chain. The unusual appearance of the Premier locomotive, which had a circular section bonnet over the engine, is noteworthy.

Among items built by John Fowler & Co Ltd during 1935 was an 0–4–0DM shunter for the LMSR, similar to GWR No 1. This locomotive (JF 21048/35) was not included in the running stock but was used by the Engineers' Department, being No 2 in the departmental stock list and subsequently becoming No 1. It was of conventional Fowler design, powered by an 88hp Ruston engine, and had a four-speed gearbox giving a top speed of 15mph, driving via jackshaft and side rods to the wheels. Its maximum tractive effort was 8,800lb. The locomotive subsequently passed into BR ownership as ED No 1, and was finally scrapped in June 1962.

A more interesting and unusual Fowler product during 1935 was the 3ft-gauge diesel mechanical unit, two of which were supplied to Associated Portland Cement Manufacturers Ltd for use at their Harbury works. These were of the 2–4–0 wheel notation and weighed 18 tons. The engine was a Ruston 6VQ engine of 106hp running at 1,000rpm. A three-speed gearbox giving speeds of 4·46, 6·92 and 11·05mph was fitted, final drive being by jackshaft and side rods. The mechanical design was straightforward and a centre cab between two Bonnet's layout was used. Main dimensions were: length 19ft 6½in, height 8ft 11in, width 7ft 8in, wheelbase 10ft, coupled wheelbase 4ft 9in. Maximum tractive effort was 7,150lb. The locomotives worked until 1970 when the Warwickshire system closed and they were moved to the same firm's Kilvington works in Nottinghamshire for possible further use. They carry works Nos 20684/5.

Delivery commenced in 1935 of the first ten of a total order of twenty placed in 1934 for 350–400hp diesel-electric shunters, ten each from Hawthorn Leslie and Armstrong Whitworth. The Hawthorn Leslie batch was delivered first and although the mechanical portions were built and erected at Newcastle, the power equipment was installed at the English Electric works at Preston, to which the mechanical portions were taken. Carrying HL works Nos 3841–50, they were numbered 7069–78 in LMSR stock. These locomotives differed from the

Fig 83 *A small standard-gauge shunter built by James C. Kay & Co Ltd trading under the name of Premier Locomotives*

prototype in that the engine was set to deliver 350 hp instead of 300hp. The same 6K engine was used to drive the main generator and supply power to two 175hp traction motors of the nose-suspended, axle-hung, self-ventilated, single reduction-gear drive type, mounted on the outer axles. Side rods coupled all three axles.

At 51 tons 9cwt, they exceeded the prototype by 2cwt, while their maximum speed was reduced to 30mph, as opposed to 35mph in the prototype. The comparative dimensions and details of these locomotives, together with those of the subsequently built Armstrong Whitworth units, are given below.

	Hawthorn Leslie– English Electric	Armstrong Whitworth
Engine hp	350	350–400
Engine rpm	700	1,000
Number of traction motors	2	1
Maximum tractive effort	30,000lb	30,000lb
Wheelbase	11ft 6in	14ft 6in
Length over buffers	28ft 6¾in	31ft 4½in
Width overall	8ft 9in	8ft 7in
Height overall	12ft 4in	12ft 6in
Fuel capacity (gal)	500	545
Maximum speed (mph)	30	23½
Weight in working order (tons)	51·9	52

During late 1940 eight of these locomotives were transferred to the War Department and sent to France, where they were lost to the enemy after the evacuation from Dunkirk. The two remaining locomotives, LMSR 7074/6, later became BR 1200/1 and they were not withdrawn from service at Crewe until May 1961 and December 1962 respectively.

Harland & Wolff were now actively engaged on design work for diesel traction and submitted numerous proposals for mainline locomotives, mobile powerhouses, shunters, etc, all using combinations of the Harland & Wolff-built Burmeister & Wain two-stroke engines. These designs were often similar to current Armstrong Whitworth proposals, no doubt because they were working on competitive tenders to similar specifications. Interesting large locomotives included a twin-engined 1–Co–Co–1 diesel-electric of 1,200hp for India, somewhat similar to the Armstrong Whitworth units built during 1935. Another design for a 2,450hp twin-engined

1–B–B–B–B–1 diesel-electric, rather similar in outline to the much later post-war Southern Railway/BR locomotives 10201/2/3, was prepared for an unknown customer.

Some twin-unit mobile powerhouses of 1,650hp and 5ft 6in gauge, running on four twin-axle bogies, were also designed, as well as others down to narrow-gauge shunting units.

After going into liquidation in November 1934, the Avonside Engine Co Ltd closed down and the company's goodwill and designs were acquired in July 1935 by the Hunslet Engine Co. Avonside's output of internal-combustion locomotives had not been of any great magnitude but the company had gained a well-earned reputation for quality of design and high standards of workmanship.

Armstrong Whitworth's first two diesel locomotives of 1935 were two small 0–4–0DE shunters. The first of these (AW D53/35) was built under order DT61, and put into service on 1 July 1935 at the Penmaenmawr mountain granite workings of the Penmaenmawr & Welsh Granite Co Ltd. Of 3ft gauge, it was designed for working at an altitude of 970ft, its work including the hauling of some 250 tons of rock per hour over 1,000–1,400yd of level track cut into the mountainside.

Power came from an Armstrong–Saurer 4BLD four-cylinder unit of 60hp, derated to 58hp at 1,700 rpm for this locomotive. Laurence Scot electrical equipment was installed, comprising a main generator and a single-frame mounted traction motor which drove via a cardan shaft to a worm-axle drive unit on the rear axle, both axles being coupled with side rods. The locomotive's main dimensions were: length 14ft 10in, height 8ft 4in, width 5ft 2in, wheelbase 3ft 6in, wheel diameter 27in. It weighed 9 tons, had a top speed of 24mph and a maximum tractive effort of 4,500lb.

The locomotive worked successfully and, apart from trouble with the worm-axle drive unit, requiring a spare unit to be kept in hand, and being rebuilt with an AEC diesel engine after World War II, it remained in use until rail traction ceased at Penmaenmawr. It was noted out of use in 1967 and, after unsuccessful attempts to have it lowered from its high altitude for preservation, it was scrapped in 1969.

Another small shunter was delivered in August 1935 to the Penang Harbour Board. This was a metre-gauge 0–4–0DE built under order DT60 at Scotswood. It carried works No D52 of 1935. Designed for shunting at Penang harbour, Straits Settlements, it worked only short distances, averaging a quarter of a mile with loads of around 40–50 tons. The engine was a six-cylinder Armstrong–Saurer 6BLD rated at 92hp at 1,700rpm.

A Laurence Scot generator supplied power to a Laurence Scot frame–mounted traction motor. The transmission, following typical AW practice, included a cardan shaft and worm-axle drive unit on leading axle, with wheels coupled by side rods. The locomotive weighed 15 tons 13cwt, and had a top speed of 25mph. Length over buffers was 17ft 6in, height 11ft, width 6ft 10in, wheelbase 5ft 6in, wheel diameter 39in. Maximum tractive effort was 8,500lb. Compared with steam traction costing 15·8d per mile, the diesel unit operated at 9·9d per mile. This locomotive worked at Penang until 1959 when the Malayan Railways took over operation of the harbour. It was then sold and in 1970 was still working at a cement works in Selangor. Armstrong Whitworth's ultimate in diesel traction appeared with the delivery to Karachi in September 1935 of two large 5ft 6in-gauge mainline locomotives for the North Western Railway of India. They were shipped in fully erected condition from Elswick works wharf.

Built under order DT51, these locomotives were powered by an eight-cylinder in-line Armstrong–Sulzer 8LD34 engine of 1,200hp at 630rpm, but in this case derated to give 984hp. The generator was by Laurence Scot and the four axle-hung, nose-suspended traction motors by Crompton Parkinson. Axle arrangement was 1A–Co–2 and the locomotives weighed 117 tons in working order. Top speed was 70mph and maximum tractive effort 39,400lb. Overall dimensions were: length over buffers 56ft 8in, height 13ft 1½in, width 9ft 10in, wheelbase—the 1A bogie wheelbase was 9ft 3in, the rigid wheelbase 4ft 3in and the final two-bogie two-axle carrying wheelbase 7ft 6in; wheel diameters—1A bogie 36in and 48in, rigid 48in, two-bogie 36in; they could negotiate curves down to 400ft radius. An auxiliary engine generator set powered by a 110hp Armstrong–Saurer 6BXD six-cylinder engine drove all the locomotive auxiliaries, leaving the whole power of the main engine for traction purposes.

The Indian Railway Board allowed £52,000 for the purchase of these locomotives. The declared intention was to run them over the Sind desert with the Karachi–Lahore mail trains, although it was suggested that the real motive was to acquire experience of mainline diesel traction in preparation for the oft-discussed direct line to connect Bombay and Karachi which, running through barren, waterless country, would present problems for steam traction.

Carrying Indian North Western Railway Nos 332 and 333, the two locomotives were put on initial trials and much trouble was experienced with flashovers at the generators and traction motors, which apparently had not had full capacity tests at Scotswood. While locomotive No 333 was being hauled dead, vibrations closed the reverser drum on the hauled locomotive's traction motors, causing the motors to generate. The result was severe damage—so much so that two of the locomotive's motors required complete rewinding and the others extensive repairs.

As repair facilities at Karachi were limited, locomotive No 332 hauled No 333, plus a 40 ton coach, to Lahore, departing on 7 October 1935 and arriving on 9 October. During the 752 miles run No 332 used 400gal of fuel.

Fig 84 *Penmaenmawr & Welsh Granite Co Ltd 0–4–0*DE *of 1935 by Armstrong Whitworth. It was scrapped in 1969,* AW D53/35 *(3ft gauge)*

Fig 85 *The ultimate in Scotswood-built diesel electric traction—the 1,200hp mainliners for the North Western Railway of India. One unit shown here in Scotswood works*

At Lahore No 333 was laid aside for repairs while tests were started on No 332 with loads of 110–350 tons on short runs, totalling about 1,000 miles. But flashovers continued even with light loads at both generators and traction motors, and grew worse as speeds rose above 50mph. Great trouble was experienced with the riding qualities, and vibrations caused much malfunctioning of electrical apparatus, such as relays. Modifications to the contactors eventually overcame this problem, and the Sulzer engines proved entirely satisfactory throughout the trials.

As a result of all these troubles, Armstrong Whitworth decided to take the whole power equipment —engines, generators and traction motors—back to Scotswood for modifications. The last trials in India were carried out in June 1936 and the power equipment sent to Scotswood. No further work was, in fact, carried out as the rumoured closure of the Diesel Traction Department became a reality early in 1937 and the North Western Railway were reluctantly persuaded to release the manufacturers from their contract. The closure of the department was said to have been due to pressure of munitions work, but it is more likely that financial considerations and the continuing lack of interest by home railways in diesel traction, caused the end of this most promising department.

Fig 86 *One of the 1,200hp Armstrong Whitworth 1A–Co–2DE units on trials at Lahore, North Western Railway of India in 1935 (5ft 6in gauge)*

The mechanical portions of Nos 332 and 333 were left in India and sold for scrap. The following figures of their limited operations are of interest:

Loco No	Main engine hours	Auxiliary engine hours	Locomotive hours	Mileage
332	182	206	241	5,102
333	51	84	70	1,387

The engines were eventually sold, through a Sulzer subsidiary, for stationary duty at the BBC's Rampisham Down establishment.

Late in 1935, E. E. Baguley Ltd built for Crossley Bros Ltd an 0–4–0DM standard-gauge shunter, which was supplied to the works of Arthur Lee & Sons Ltd, steelworks, Sheffield. The mechanical portion followed standard Baguley practice, but the power unit was the Crossley two-cylinder, two-stroke engine of 55hp at 550rpm. The transmission incorporated the Baguley two-speed epicyclic gearbox, the final drive being taken from a front-mounted transverse shaft with chains to the leading axle. This unit (BG 2087/35), which weighed 12 tons, had speeds of 3·5 and 6mph and a maximum tractive effort of 4,400lb. Overall dimensions were: length 16ft 7½in, height 9ft 10¾in, width 7ft, wheelbase 5ft 6in, wheel diameter 37in. The locomotive was scrapped in 1960.

CHAPTER 8

1936-1940: MAINLY SHUNTERS

A NEWCOMER to diesel traction during 1936 was the Vulcan Foundry Ltd of Newton-le-Willows, Lancashire, who had taken out a licence from the Frichs Company of Denmark to build the Frichs diesel engine for locomotive use.

Vulcan's first locomotive was an 0–6–0DM unit designed to be suitable for use as a shunter or for local goods and passenger work. Powered by a Vulcan–Frichs type diesel engine, which in this first application was built by Frichs at Aarhus, Denmark, it was of type 6215CL with six cylinders in line rated at 275hp at 775rpm, and could be run at 300 hp for short periods.

The transmission consisted of a Vulcan–Sinclair fluid coupling, a Wilson five-speed epicyclic gearbox giving speeds of 4·57, 11·4, 21·3, 32·6 and 46 mph, a David Brown reverse gearbox and double reduction gear, jackshaft final drive and side rods. The engine was air-started, using air stored while the engine was running, and an additional starting compressor powered by a single-cylinder Lister petrol engine. Weight in working order was 47·5 tons, the maximum tractive effort being 20,310lb. Overall dimensions were: length 28ft 4½in, width 8ft 8½in, wheelbase 12ft, wheel diameter 48in.

Built as a prototype, after lengthy initial service in the makers' works yard, the locomotive (VF 4564/34) was sent out on loan and demonstration. It worked on the LMSR at Crewe and was eventually taken over by the WD in 1939 as WD No 75, later 4564. It was reconditioned and sold after the war to the Svetozarevo Cable works in Yugoslavia.

The only other application by Vulcan of the Frichs engine was in ten diesel railcars built in 1939–40 for New Zealand Government Railways.

By now, Andrew Barclay Sons & Co Ltd were starting to produce a slow but steady stream of diesel shunting locomotives of good design, and these continued to be built until well after World War II without much design change. Typical were two for the Air Ministry in 1936 which, apart from being characteristic of Barclay's current designs, were interesting in that they were powered by a Scottish-built diesel engine. This engine, the Gleniffer, was an eight-cylinder unit rated at 160hp and was rarely applied to rail traction. The transmission included a Vulcan–Sinclair fluid coupling, a Wilson epicyclic gearbox, and Bostock & Bramley forward and reverse gears. Final drive was by jackshaft and side rods. Weight of the locomotive in working order was 22¾ tons and the two supplied to the Air Ministry carried works Nos AB 321 and 322 of 1936.

Fig 87 *The unique Vulcan–Frichs 0–6–0DM of 1934 built for demonstration, and eventually sold for service in Yugoslavia, VF 4564/34*

Fig 88 *A typical standard Barclay shunter of the post-1935 period. This example is one of two with Gleniffer 160hp engines, and 0–4–0DM layout for the Air Ministry—* AB 321/2 of 1936

The year 1936 was a really notable one for shunters, activity being centred on Tyneside's locomotive builders, Hawthorn Leslie and Armstrong Whitworth. The Hawthorn Leslie contribution consisted of further English Electric-equipped units of the now accepted design. One of these units (HL 3853/35) was supplied to the GWR in April 1936 under Swindon Lot No 302. Painted in GWR livery, it was numbered No 2 with, unusually, a number painted on, in the GWR internal-combustion series, No 1 being the Fowler unit of 1933, and never in fact carried a GWR numberplate. This locomotive was generally similar to the LMSR shunters completed in the final deliveries in 1936.

The GWR unit was heavier at 51 tons 11cwt, or 2cwt more than the LMSR units, and its top speed was limited to 19mph compared with 30mph for the LMSR units. It took up work in Acton yard. Later it worked mainly at Bristol but as BR No 15100, which it became in February 1948, was withdrawn from Swindon shed in April 1965. During the war it was on loan to the WD, who used it to shunt oil refinery sidings in the Swansea area.

Two more Hawthorn Leslie examples in 1936 were built for the Sudan Government Railways, who gave them Nos 401 and 402. These 3ft 6in-gauge units (HL 3854/55 of 1936) were put into traffic during the autumn and after several months at Atbara for initial trials were moved to Port Sudan. Here they were used on heavy continuous shunting duties, working twenty-four hours per day, six days per week, normally handling loads of up to 900 tons. From the time of being put into traffic until the end of 1939, locomotive No 401 had been in service 16,100hr, and No 402 13,800hr,

operating costs being less than 50 per cent of that for steam power. Again, as on the LMSR and GWR, the English Electric 6K engine, English Electric generator and traction motors were used. Weighing 45.75 tons, these shunters had a maximum tractive effort of 28,000lb. Overal dimensions were: length 28ft 10½in, height 12ft 9in, width 10ft 2in, wheelbase 11ft 6in, wheel diameter 51in.

Three more 3ft 6in-gauge units were built by Hawthorn Leslie in 1936 for New Consolidated Goldfields Ltd, South Africa. These were works Nos 3866–8 of 1936.

The range of diesel-electric shunters by the English Electric–Hawthorn Leslie association included three- and four-axle units with either inside or outside frames and also a Bo–Bo type, all of which were very similar in external appearance. Only three-axle units were, however, actually built.

Armstrong Whitworth's contribution to this diesel electric shunter activity was the delivery between May 1935 and November 1936 of ten units ordered by the LMSR in 1935 under order No DT63, works Nos D54–63. Built for comparison trials with the Hawthorn Leslie–English Electric 350hp units already in service, they differed considerably from these in that they followed the standard AW design for large shunters, and were based on the 250hp 0–6–0DE design, in fact an enlargement of this design, of which two were built.

A feature of the design was that the bonnet, in addition to housing as usual the engine, generator and radiator, also housed the single traction motor with double reduction gear drive, which drove to the wheels by being placed directly over the jackshaft unit. The placing of the drive arrangement

Fig 89 LMSR 7059–68. The Armstrong Whitworth 400hp 0–6–0DE of 1936, all of which passed to WD ownership, AW D54–63. One similar unit was supplied to India in 1936

within the locomotive's wheelbase did, of course, require unequal spacing of the wheels and resulted in a total wheelbase of 14ft 6in as opposed to 11ft 6in on the English Electric–Hawthorn Leslie units. This presented problems when working on sharply curved lines, so the necessary flexibility was gained by allowing ¼in side play on the centre wheels.

The engine used was the Armstrong–Sulzer LTD22 six-cylinder in-line type, developing 400hp at 1,000rpm. The electrical equipment was by Crompton Parkinson. (A table of comparative details of the English Electric–Hawthorn Leslie locomotives may be found on p 96.)

The locomotives were placed in service on heavy yard shunting work at Willesden, Crewe and Carlisle, where they operated with complete success. Between 1940 and 1945, all ten locomotives were transferred to the War Department and eight of them sent overseas, Nos 7060/65/6/8 going to the Middle East to Suez and apparently remaining there, while Nos 7059/61/4/7, after service in Europe and being on loan to the Netherlands Railways, were in 1946 purchased by Belgian State Railways to become Class 230, Nos 01–04, working at Antwerp. They put in some good work and, apart from being modified for air brakes, were little altered. The remaining two, Nos 7062/3, remained in the United Kingdom, becoming eventually WD 882/3, and were taken out of stock in 1968. They have since seen further use by contractors and one or both may still be extant.

Another shunter of similar design was delivered by Armstrong Whitworth in October 1936 to the Bombay Baroda & Central India Railway under order DT68. Built to the Indian loading gauge, this 5ft 6in-gauge unit employed the same power equipment as the LMSR units, but with the Sulzer engine derated to 350hp. Overall dimensions of this 48 ton locomotive were: length over buffers 32ft 6in,

height 12ft 7$\frac{9}{16}$in, width 10ft, wheelbase 14ft 6in, wheel diameter 43in. The top speed was 22mph and it had a maximum tractive effort of 24,000lb. The locomotive was put to work on continuous service in the Bandra Hump yard, Bombay.

Fairly typical among the smaller Drewry locomotives built by E. E. Baguley Ltd, Burton-on-Trent, was a 2ft 6in-gauge petrol locomotive for the War Office, for use on the rail system of the Royal Small Arms School at Hythe. Delivered in October 1936, this 3 ton unit had a 24hp Ford petrol engine and a Baguley three-speed gearbox and chain-drive transmission. Its task was target towing and it carried works No 2094/36.

Other similar locomotives (DC 2104/5) were supplied in the following year to Cornwall County Council for use at their Tolpetherwin Quarry near Launceston, remaining there until 1949 when they were sold to J. Pugsley & Sons Ltd of Bristol, contractors' plant dealers. These 2ft-gauge units had 25hp three-cylinder Ailsa Craig diesel engines and Baguley transmissions with chain drive and were built by E. E. Baguley for the Drewry Car Co.

The most powerful of the Bagnall–Deutz type industrial diesels were two narrow-gauge units delivered in 1937. The first (WGB 2567/37) of 2ft 6in gauge was supplied to the African Manganese Co and had Westinghouse brakes. It cost £2,095 and was delivered in February. The second (WGB 2573/37) was of 2ft gauge and in April 1937 was shipped to Durban for estate use by Sir J. L. Hulett & Sons at Darnall. This unit cost £1,950, had air brakes and electric lighting, and was still at work in March 1954. Both were powered by Deutz two-stroke three-cylinder engines of 110–120hp at 450 rpm. A Bagnall four-speed gearbox was fitted and final drive was by jackshaft and side rods. Weighing 8 tons, they had a tractive effort of 8,200lb at 4·35mph.

The only standard-gauge Deutz-engined Bagnall-built shunter was delivered in June 1937 to F. H. Lloyd & Co Ltd, Wednesbury, for use at their steelworks. This unit (WGB 2577/37) had a 77hp engine with the usual four-speed gearbox and jack-shaft and side-rod drive. Costing £1,875, it weighed 22 tons and worked until the mid-1950s, being scrapped in 1957.

The 0–6–0 diesel mechanical locomotive (HE 1846/37) delivered to the War Department at Corsham, Wiltshire, in March 1937 and numbered 1 (later WD 846), may be considered the prototype for the 204hp three-axle shunter introduced during the war years and since sold in large numbers. The engine was a Gardner 8L3 eight-cylinder unit set to give 155hp at 1,000rpm, with a short-time maximum of 170hp. A Hunslet plate clutch drove to a Hunslet patent hydraulically operated preselective gearbox of three-speed type (5, 9 and 15mph). Final drive was by jackshaft and side rods. Weight in working order was 22 tons 3cwt. Overall dimensions were: length 19ft 8in, height 9ft, width 8ft 8in, wheelbase 8ft, wheel diameter 36in. The locomotive is now with the Tunnel Portland Cement Co Ltd, Gartsherrie, Lanarkshire.

Further activity by Harland & Wolff Ltd resulted in two locomotives for use in Northern Ireland on 5ft 3in-gauge lines. Order No 9825 was for a relatively large three-axle diesel hydraulic locomotive for the Northern Counties Committee of the LMSR, powered as usual by the Harland–Burmeister & Wain two-stroke type engine, in this case an eight-cylinder in-line TR8, set to produce 330hp at 1,200 rpm.

The transmission used, the first application of its kind to a British-built locomotive, was the Voith type, supplied by Vulcan–Sinclair, who at that time were the British licensees. The transmission was of the turbo type, size 36, later styled L306 and then L630, and was used in many post-World War II mainline diesel hydraulics on British Railways mainly by the North British Locomotive Co.

A two-speed reverse and reduction gearbox was fitted and final drive was by jackshaft and side rods. The main engine was started by a single-cylinder 2½hp petrol engine. Weight in working order was 49·65 tons; top speed was 50mph and maximum tractive effort 24,000lb. Main overall dimensions were: length over buffers 32ft 4½in, height 12ft 8in, width 9ft 4in, wheelbase 12ft, wheel diameter 49½in.

Numbered 17 by the NCC, the locomotive was designed to be suitable for passenger, shunting and goods work, hence its relatively high speed. It passed eventually to the Ulster Transport Authority, and is still in use with Northern Ireland Railways.

The Belfast & County Down Railway, already operating a Harland & Wolff diesel locomotive on mixed traffic branch-line duty, took delivery of a much larger second unit for express passenger duty. This double bogie unit, H & W order No 10170, was put into stock during 1937 as No 28 in the B & CDR stock. Designed under the direction of the railway's locomotive engineer, Mr J. L. Crosthwait, for use on the 8 mile long Ardglass branch which had 1 in 50 gradients and severe curvature in its route, it had a Clarkson exhaust-gas train-heating boiler fitted.

The engine was a Harland B & W two-stroke TR8 eight-cylinder diesel developing 500hp at 825rpm.

Fig 90 *The only standard-gauge Bagnall–Deutz shunter was this 77hp 0–4–0*DM *for F. H. Lloyd & Co of Wednesbury,* WB 2577/37

Fig 91 *The second Harland & Wolff diesel for the* B & CDR. *A 500hp 1A–A1* DE *for the Ardglass branch in 1937 (5ft 3in gauge)*

A Laurence Scot main generator supplied power to two Laurence Scot nose-suspended, axle-hung, self-ventilated traction motors, situated only on the inner axle of each two-axle bogie, so giving the locomotive an axle arrangement of 1A–A1. Weight in working order was 48 tons, maximum axle load 12·362 tons, top speed 55mph, maximum tractive effort 10,000lb; overall dimensions were: length 36ft 5½in, height 12ft 5 3/16 in, width 9ft, bogie wheelbase 7ft, bogie centres 16ft, wheel diameter 43in. This locomotive passed to the UTA who are thought to have it still.

The now almost traditional practice, peculiar largely to the British railway system, of railways building their own diesel locomotive mechanical parts was initiated by the Ashford works of the Southern Railway in 1937 when they built three diesel-electric shunting locomotives. Completed under order A936, they were, like the Hawthorn Leslie–English Electric LMSR shunters, sent to the English Electric Preston works to have their power equipment installed.

The standard English Electric 6K type six-cylinder engine was fitted, giving 350hp at 680rpm, plus an English Electric main generator of slightly larger size than that of the LMSR units, and two axle-hung, nose-suspended, force-ventilated traction motors with single reduction gear drive of the same make on the two outer axles, all axles being coupled.

These units, designed by O. V. S. Bulleid, had larger wheels, 54in in diameter, and weighed 55·3 tons in working order, top speed being 30mph and maximum tractive effort 30,000lb. The mechanical portion included variations to suit the railway's individual requirements, ie the larger wheels were required to enable the fly-cranks to clear the third rails of the SR electric system.

Numbered 1–3 by the SR, they became BR 15201–3 and spent the major part of their life at Norwood

Junction and Hither Green depots, with spells at Eastleigh, Old Oak Common and Tyseley under BR ownership. During the war, from 1941 to mid-1945, they were on loan to the War Department. They were withdrawn from service in November and December 1964.

Although orders for diesel-electric rail traction units were still being completed at Scotswood, the Diesel Traction Department of Armstrong Whitworths was now 'out of business', in that no new orders were being accepted and the work was rapidly drawing to a close.

Among locomotives held at Scotswood awaiting purchasers were the ill-fated Universal locomotives of 1934, which had been on hand since the completion of the trials in Ceylon during 1935. These had been overhauled and were available for sale to anyone interested, but their gauge of 5ft 6in somewhat limited their scope. Their salvation came in 1937 when an old-established diesel customer of AW came to the rescue, namely the Buenos Aires Great Southern Railway (BAGSR). They were sold under Scotswood order No DT74, becoming CM 204 and CM205 in BAGSR stock.

After initial trials, the locomotives commenced operation on the same service as the twin unit of 1,700hp which AW supplied in 1932, working alternate nights with the overnight trains between Buenos Aires and Bahia Blanca in 1938. They operated satisfactorily for some 30,900 miles, with running and fuel costs similar to the 1,700hp unit.

Having been designed originally for use in dry and dusty conditions requiring every engine and electrical compartment window and door to be closed at all times, air was admitted only by drawing it in through felt filters in the locomotive electrical compartment sides. The air was then drawn into the rest of the engine room by the generator fan. Frequently the filters became blocked, causing high temperatures inside the locomotives. Replacement of felt with fine wire gauze filters made a great improvement and, in addition, the engine exhaust silencer was moved outside the locomotive and new ventilators provided in the engine room roof. All this resulted in improved operating conditions and it was no longer necessary to wait for the locomotives to cool down before any work could be undertaken in the engine compartment.

Great trouble was, however, experienced with the auxiliary engine/generator, which was the direct cause of failure in three out of every four cases, and the wisdom of providing such equipment was questionable. Engine trouble, attributable to piston design, caused the railway to reduce the engine horsepower from 800 to 600, which enabled the locomotives to continue working in multiple on the overnight Buenos Aires–Bahia Blanca trains, until one locomotive failed in 1939.

This unit, CM205, sustained severe engine damage when a piston-connecting rod bolt broke. The bolt damaged the connecting rod which, in turn, distorted the engine crankcase and fractured the cylinder block. The locomotive was no longer usable and was put in store while the cylinder block and crankcase were sent to Switzerland for repairs which, due to hostilities, were delayed.

The remaining locomotive, CM204, was found to be difficult to employ owing to its reduced power and the fact that trains were becoming heavier because of wartime conditions and reduction of service frequency. It was found employment, however, together with CM206, one of the 1938 Harland & Wolff units, on the milk train service between Canuelas and Buenos Aires, working the trips alternately three times each day. This operation continued until September 1943 when CM204 caught fire, causing extensive damage to the engine room and its equipment. The fire was believed to have been caused by oil leakages and the ignition of adhering combustible materials by sparks from the brake blocks. This locomotive, too, was put in store for the duration of the war as replacement power equipment was unobtainable. Both units appear to have been scrapped without any attention to repairs at a latter date.

Other locomotives remaining at Scotswood were the 1933 prototype Universal unit, which had been in store since its trials on the LNER in 1934; it was scrapped in 1937. A number of order DT22 0–4–0DE shunters were still in stock, all of which eventually sold. The final locomotive was the original 1932 95hp 0–4–0DE shunter of order DT11,

which was kept on as the works yard locomotive for many years.

Quite a number of designs for diesel-electric locomotives were submitted by Armstrong Whitworths and these included various bogie locomotives, all with Sulzer engines, for such railways as Victorian Government Railways, South African Railways, Argentine Railways, BAGSR, and a special design for the London Underground. Others were for railcars and articulated train sets, powerhouses, etc, not all of which employed electric transmissions.

Hawthorn Leslie's only diesel locomotive of 1937 was one delivered in November to Thos Firth & John Brown Ltd, Sheffield. This machine (HL 3913/37) is quite familiar and was the forerunner of what was hoped would become a new range of diesel mechanical locomotives with Crossley engines from Forth Banks works. Of standardgauge, it was a two-axle unit weighing 22·4 tons and was reduced in height to 7ft 3in in view of the restricted clearance areas of the owners' steelworks. The driver's cab was located in a well at the rear and the four-cylinder, two-stroke Crossley directreversing engine developed 110hp at 500rpm. Its transmission employed a Vulcan–Sinclair hydraulic coupling and a Hawthorn Leslie two-speed gearbox, giving speeds of 3 and 6mph. Final drive was by jackshaft and side rods. An auxiliary petrol/paraffin engine was installed to drive an air compressor used to charge the air bottles for engine-starting purposes.

The locomotive had a wheelbase of 6ft 3in, wheel diameter of 37in and a maximum tractive effort of 11,700lb. It was numbered 'Firth Brown No 25', becoming later D1. It ended its days on Canklow Tip and was finally scrapped in 1967.

One of the first of the Barclay three-axle shunters was that delivered during 1937 to the Nobels Explosive Co Ltd, an ICI subsidiary at Ardeer in Ayrshire, Scotland. Power was provided by a Paxman–Ricardo eight-cylinder engine giving 180hp at 1,100rpm. The transmission was the excellent combination of the Vulcan–Sinclair fluid coupling, Wilson epicyclic three-speed gearbox with the final drive by a Bostock & Bramley drive and reverse box, with jackshaft and side rod drive. The locomotive weighed 29·5 tons and had a top speed of 12mph. At its low speed of 4mph, its tractive effort was 12,650lb. This unit (AB 323/37) is now at the Dalmuir works of Arnott Young & Co, to whom it was sold in September 1953.

War Office interest in the robust Barclay standard shunter range started in 1936 when they ordered two 0–4–0DM units fitted with 150hp

Fig 92 *An unusual Planet design, a Hibberd-built 0–4–0DM for Lake View & Star Ltd, South Africa,* FH *1938/37*

Gardner 6L3 six-cylinder engines running at 1,200 rpm. These two examples carried works Nos 324 and 325 and were delivered in 1937 to Woolwich Arsenal, where they were named *George* and *Elizabeth*. They incorporated the Vulcan–Sinclair/ Wilson/Bostock & Bramley transmission arrangement and weighed 21 tons in running order. Further examples for the War Office and Air Ministry followed, of both two- and three-axle types, with various engines. As usual, the Barclay 'chimney' exhaust arrangement was fitted.

An unusual Planet design of this period was the 2ft-gauge 0–4–0DM built for Lake View & Star Ltd, South Africa, who were a subsidiary of New Consolidated Goldfields. This somewhat hybrid machine was virtually a scaled-down Howard design, but employed plate-type main frames and jackshaft and side-rod final drive. Although supplied with a 65hp Paxman engine, it was further noteworthy as being subsequently powered by a four-cylinder Atlantic oil engine developing 70hp at 800rpm. This was one of the first applications of an Atlantic Engine Co product to rail traction. The locomotive weighed 12 tons and was fitted with a three-speed gearbox giving 3, 5 and 8mph. The production of plate-framed locomotives by Hibberds was a rare occurrence, the result often resembling work by Hudswell Clarke and John Fowler.

The year 1938 was the last in the period prior to World War II in which any British builder built mainline diesel locomotives.

The Harland & Wolff mainliners for the BAGSR were completed at Belfast under order 11517 in this year. Numbered CM206 and 207 by the railway, these two massive machines, 5ft 6in gauge of course, weighed 103·85 tons and employed a steam locomotive-type plate frame underframe containing the four driving axles, each with its own traction motor, and at each end a pony truck, giving them the axle arrangement of 1–Do–1. An overall body was fitted with driving positions at both ends.

The power unit comprised two Harland B & W TR8 eight-cylinder vertical two-stroke engines of 450hp at 800rpm, giving 900 total hp. These each drove a Brown-Boveri generator which supplied power to four Laurence Scot nose-suspended, axle-hung, force-ventilated traction motors, each of 250hp. Overall length was 49ft 11½in, height 14ft, width 10ft 6in, total wheelbase 37ft, driving wheel diameter 55½in, pony truck wheel diameter 41in. Minimum curve negotiable was 328ft, and maximum tractive effort 30,000lb.

Both locomotives were shipped to Buenos Aires fully erected. Their 103 tons weight caused great difficulty in unloading, two floating cranes having to be employed. From the outset troubles occurred in the initial trials and continual replacement of parts, due mainly to unsuitable design and materials, was necessary. Fortunately, the Harland & Wolff representatives were present and all faults were quickly rectified as they arose.

The engine trouble mainly involved the pistons and there were frequent failures at first. Fuel-admission difficulties, resulting in burnt piston heads, were also common. New pistons of improved design were fitted, together with new fuel-admission sprayers, which were a great improvement on the originals. The heavy weight of engine components caused stress troubles, which only ceased when new lightweight replacement components were fitted.

Traction motor troubles necessitated their removal for attention, and the auxiliary equipment also caused many problems.

Finally it was decided to work the locomotives at less power than their designed output, so the controllers were arranged to limit the power of the engine, with great benefit to performance and reliability.

For one locomotive trains did not exceed 250–300 tons weight, and CM206 so modified operated much more successfully. Before any modifications could be carried out on CM207, it caught fire in October 1941 and had to be laid aside until spares could be obtained at the end of the war. Unit CM206 continued in service and was still at work in 1945. The original intention to use these locomotives in multiple was never carried out.

The final locomotive product of Harland & Wolff appeared in 1938 in the form of a small 0–4–0DM shunter for use in the firm's works yards at Belfast. Built under order No 11612, it had a Harland B & W TR6 six-cylinder two-stroke engine of 225hp at 1,200rpm. The mechanical transmission included a Vulcan–Sinclair coupling and an SLM four-speed gearbox, drive to the wheels being by jackshaft and side rods. Weight in working order was 28·31 tons, speed range 4·41, 7·65, 12·1 and 20mph, with a maximum tractive effort of 15,000lb. Length overall was 23ft 4½in, height 12ft 1½in, width 9ft, wheelbase 8ft, wheel diameter 43in. Starting was by a 2½hp petrol/paraffin engine. It was later sold to the NCC and then passed to the UTA who still use it as No 16 in their stock.

An interesting contract carried out by the Drewry Car Co was the building by the English Electric Dick Kerr works at Preston of seven 3ft 6in-gauge

0–6–0 mechanical portions with Vulcan–Sinclair–Wilson transmissions and jackshaft and side-rod drive. These locomotives (DC 2121–7) were built for the New Zealand Government Railways without engines to utilise a number of Leyland 10 litre petrol engines removed from some unsuccessful railcars. One engine was shipped to England for trials in a locomotive prior to the shipment of the whole batch. The remaining six locomotives had their engines installed in New Zealand.

As road vehicle manufacturers, AEC (Associated Equipment Company Ltd) were very well established, and in 1938 they tried to re-enter the railway shunting market by offering a basic two-axle unit in two sizes, 78 and 115hp, displaying obvious lineage with Hardy Motors' work.

One example of the 78hp unit was built at Southall. The engine was a four-cylinder unit with an AEC clutch, four-speed gearbox and countershaft drive to both axles. Weighing 13·3 tons, its overall length was 18ft 1½in, height 11ft 4in, width 8ft 1in, wheelbase 7ft 6in, wheel diameter 37in. The tractive effort at 2·7mph was 8,850lb and top speed 11·9mph. The 78hp example remains in use today at the AEC Southall works and no others were ever built.

During eight months in service it handled 1,469 loaded and 139 empty wagons of inward traffic, and 616 loaded and 972 empty of outward traffic. Service hours were 563, and 976 miles were covered, fuel consumption averaging 0·492gal per service hour. Tests on the GWR Brentford branch line revealed that the locomotive could easily handle a 77-wagon train of up to 900 tons at 2·3mph.

The centre-cab design of Fowler diesel shunting locomotives started to gain some popularity and

Fig 93 *The largest of Harland & Wolff's rail traction work were these two 1–Do–1*DE *units of 900hp for the* BAGSR *in 1938 (5ft 6in gauge)*

Fig 94 *The solitary* AEC-*built shunter of 78hp produced in 1938*

both narrow- and standard-gauge examples were soon at work from around 1932. Roads Reconstruction Ltd took delivery of a standard-gauge example in 1932. This was a 25 ton unit with two axles (JF 19645/32) powered by a Fowler–Sanders engine with four cylinders giving 100hp at 1,000rpm. The transmission was of Fowler design, giving four speeds and having final drive by jackshaft and side rods. It was put to work at Vobster Limestone Quarry in Somerset.

Larger versions were built, also one with three axles, typified by the example built in 1938 for Richard Thomas & Co Ltd for special duties at their Ebbw Vale steelworks. It was supplied to haul a heavy iron-ore dumping transfer car over a short run. This unit (JF 22497/38) weighed 31 tons and was Fowler–Sanders-powered by a four-

cylinder 150hp engine running at 1,000rpm. The Fowler transmission incorporated a multiple-disc dry friction clutch and four-speed gearbox of the constant-mesh type, giving speeds of 3, 6, 10 and 15mph. Final drive was by jackshaft and side rods, maximum tractive effort was 13,000lb and starting was by a 14hp two-cylinder Fowler–Sanders petrol engine. Length over buffers was 25ft 6in, wheelbase 8ft 6in, wheel diameter 39in.

The Hunslet Engine Co's second bogie diesel locomotive was delivered in June 1938 to Patrick Murray (PTY) Ltd for Doornkop Sugar Estate, Natal. This 2ft-gauge unit (HE 1877/38) differed somewhat from the Woolwich Arsenal unit of 1934 and in its final drive arrangement was more in line with Avonside practice.

Powered by a McLaren engine similar to the

Fig 95 *A Fowler-built centre-cab 0–6–0*DM *for Richard Thomas & Co, Ebbw Vale, powered by a 150hp Fowler–Sanders engine,* JF 22497/38

1934 unit of 75–82hp, the transmission was taken this time to a centrally mounted three-speed gearbox with cardan shafts, to an axle drive worm unit on the outer axle of each bogie, both axles on each bogie being rod coupled. Weight in working order was 12 tons 19cwt, speed range was 4·19, 7·84 and 11·5mph, and maximum tractive effort at starting was 6,270lb. It was 15ft 2½in in overall length, height was 9ft 10$\frac{1}{16}$in, width 6ft 3½in, bogie wheelbase 3ft, wheel diameter 20in.

Typical among the larger Drewry Car Co diesel locomotives built for overseas by the English Electric works at Preston were some two-axle and three-axle units of 2ft gauge for the Eagle Oil Co Ltd in Mexico. These incorporated Gardner engines and the Vulcan–Sinclair–Wilson system of transmission which was so popular with Drewrys.

A 3ft 6in gauge 0–4–0DM (DC 2097/38) was supplied to the Ohai Railway Board, New Zealand. This Preston-built example had the standard transmission as used on the Eagle Oil locomotives and a Gardner type 6LW engine.

Hudswell Clarke had by this time evolved their basic diesel locomotive design which was to remain standard until well after World War II. Typical features were the end cab, bonnet well back from front buffer beam, small steam-type chimney for engine exhaust, and in some cases an oil tank behind the cab reminiscent of a steam locomotive coal bunker. A front-end-mounted jackshaft final drive unit with side rod drive, similar to Fowler's one-time designs, was another typical feature.

The Bede Metal & Chemical Co Ltd of Hebburn took delivery in 1938 of an 0–4–0DM (HC D607/38) of 125hp. Fitted with a McLaren six-cylinder 6MDBX engine, it had a Vulcan–Sinclair fluid coupling, and a three-speed gearbox; final drive was by jackshaft and side rods. Overall dimensions were: length 24ft, height 10ft 6in, width 7ft 8in, wheelbase 5ft 9in, wheel diameter 33½in. Weighing 25 tons, it had speeds of 3½, 5¼ and 10mph and a maximum tractive effort of 10,710lb at 3½mph.

One of the largest Planet locomotives was delivered in 1938 from the Hibberd Southall works to Crossley-Premier Engines Ltd, Sandiacre. This standard-gauge 0–4–0DM bore a likeness to Hudswell Clarke's then current practice, and others of even greater similarity to the Leeds firm's current models followed. The locomotive in question, however, had a Crossley two-stroke, three-cylinder in-line engine of 82hp at 500rpm. The transmission was considered quite an advance on current Planet practice in that it incorporated an automatic gear change. The Freeborn gearbox with its automatic gear changing feature cut out most driving controls, leaving only the throttle, reverse and brake handles. Breaks in tractive effort at each gear-change were practically nil and five gear speeds were included—3, 4, 5½, 7½ and 10mph. Final drive was by jackshaft and side rods. Weighing 23 tons, it was 21ft 9½in in overall length, height was 10ft 8½in, wheelbase 6ft. Preliminary trials included a short period at an LMSR sleeper depot before delivery and thorough service trials. It was scrapped in 1959.

The last diesel-electric locomotive order carried out by the Hawthorn Leslie–English Electric association was that for three mainline metre-gauge mixed traffic units for the Eastern Railway of Brazil in 1938, the order being delivered in September of that year. These locomotives were of the Bonnet

Fig 96 The standard Hudswell Clarke shunter is typified by this 125hp 0–4–0DM for the Bede Metal & Chemical Co of Hebburn-on-Tyne, HC D607/38

Fig 97 *An unusual Planet 0–4–0DM supplied to Crossley-Premier Engines Ltd of Sandiacre in 1938*

type with a cab at one end, the underframe being rigid in the centre with four driven axles and a pony truck at each end, giving an axle layout of 1–B–B–1.

The engine fitted was a 450hp English Electric 8K, an 8-cylinder in-line unit. This drove an English Electric generator which powered two force-ventilated, axle-hung, nose-suspended traction motors on the outer axles with coupling rods to the other axles. The power equipment was installed at the English Electric works at Preston and the locomotive's weight in working order was 55 tons.

The works numbers of the first two were HL 3947/8, but the third example was RSH 6947,

because by the time it was finished the firms of Hawthorn Leslie and Robert Stephenson & Co had amalgamated. The three locomotives were set to work with trains of specially-built passenger stock and are thought to be still in service.

Another Hawthorn Leslie design, of which only two were built under that name, was their new standard 0–4–0DM shunting locomotive with a Crossley engine. This was a five-cylinder two-stroke unit of 150hp running at 550rpm. The transmission was quite orthodox and included a Vulcan–Sinclair coupling, two-speed gearbox giving 4 and 8mph and a jackshaft and side-rod final drive unit at the front end of the locomotive. Carrying works Nos

Fig 98 *The Hawthorn Leslie–English Electric 450hp 1–B–B–1DE for the Eastern Railway of Brazil in 1938. HL 3947/8 of 1938 and RSH 6941/39 (Metre gauge)*

3949/50 of 1939, they were both delivered in January to the Royal Ordnance factory at Chorley as ROF 3 and ROF 4. These locomotives were followed by further batches from Forth Banks works during 1939–40 after the amalgamation of Robert Stephenson & Hawthorns. Both locomotives were scrapped in 1966.

William Beardmore & Co Ltd, Parkhead Steelworks, Glasgow, took delivery in 1939 of two standard-gauge Barclay diesel mechanical shunters. Following standard Barclay design practice, they had, rather surprisingly, unusual power units—Beardmore diesel engines which had remained in store unsold for some years since the cessation of engine manufacture by the Beardmore group.

These engines were six-cylinder in-line type units originally built to operate at 350–75hp, but were derated to 260hp at 700rpm in this application. The transmission included a Vulcan–Sinclair fluid coupling, a Beardmore–David Brown three-speed gearbox, giving 4, 7½ and 12mph, and final drive by jackshaft and side rods. Weighing 34½ tons, they had a maximum tractive effort of 19,800lb and were 25ft 8in in overall length. Height was 11ft 11in, width 8ft 2in, wheelbase 6ft 3in, wheel diameter 41in, and they were the heaviest and most powerful Barclay diesels built up to that time.

They carried works Nos 326 of 1938, and 327 of 1939, in the Barclay list, and both are now scrapped, 326 having been sold after the war to Connells of Coatbridge for scrap, and 327 having been destroyed during the war in an air raid.

This was the final application of the Beardmore engine to rail traction but it is noteworthy here that by the end of production in 1934 it had found wide use overseas. Locomotive applications totalled only eight, the Canadian National Railways having the 2,600hp twin-unit monster and one 400hp shunter, the BAGSR one 375hp locomotive-cum-baggage unit, the Indian State Railway the two Beardmore-built units of 1930, and three industrial shunters remaining in the United Kingdom.

Railcar applications were more extensive, Canadian National again taking the largest share with twenty-eight units, and other cars going to work in Spain, Venezuela and Rumania.

Some fifty engines were built altogether in the 90–1,330hp range, of which about twelve were for non-traction use. Westinghouse in the USA took out a licence and supplied a limited number of Westinghouse–Beardmore engines, some of which were built in Scotland for them.

The most interesting delivery of 1939 was that to the Peruvian Corporation by the Hunslet Engine Co, who shipped a special diesel mechanical locomotive for use on the Guaqui–La Paz electrified railway. This railway, with gradients of up to 1 in 14, had been electrified in 1905, but diesel traction was now being tried to see if it could handle the work at no greater, and possibly less cost, and so save the railway from having to replace the almost obsolete overhead electric system by a new and expensive electrification programme.

The locomotive in question (HE 1904/39) was a metre-gauge 0–6–0DM unit fitted with a Mirrlees–Ricardo UD5 five-cylinder four-stroke engine of 330hp, but derated to 242hp at 900rpm. The engine was pressure charged by a Büchi exhaust-gas turbo-pressure charger so that the engine output would remain the same, or at least adequate,

Fig 99 One of the two Hawthorn Leslie 0–4–0DM for the Chorley Ordnance factory in 1939, HL 3949/50 of 1939

Fig 100 *The first successful high-altitude diesel—the massive Hunslet metre-gauge unit for Guaqui–La Paz railway*, HE 1904/39

at the site altitudes of 10,000–13,395ft above sea level. At sea level the Büchi turbo charger was nominally capable of increasing engine output to 500hp, but this was not the intention, and the control of the fuel injection suitably derated the engines to 220–40hp, the turbo charger being used to maintain this power at altitudes of up to 14,000ft with normal running speed.

The mechanical transmission had a Vulcan–Sinclair fluid coupling, a Hunslet auxiliary gear-change clutch, cardan shaft and Hardy–Spicer flexible coupling to a four-speed Hunslet constant-mesh gearbox. The final drive was by jackshaft and side rods. The speed range was 4·83, 7·5, 11·0 and 16·6 mph, with a maximum tractive effort of 15,950lb. Weight in working order was 39 tons and the maximum axle load 13 tons. Length over buffers was 25ft 3in, height 12ft 9¼in, width 9ft, wheelbase 10ft, wheel diameter 46in.

Two sets of independent starting equipment were fitted so that whatever extremes of temperature were met the main engine could be started. The main set, a diesel compressor set, comprised a 25hp Ailsa-Craig four-stroke engine derated to give 12½hp at working altitudes. This was electrically started, but hand starting was also provided for. The emergency starting set comprised a Ford V8 petrol engine and Bendix gear meshing onto the flywheel of the locomotive's power unit. This unit, capable of 95hp, was electrically started, but hand starting was fitted here, too.

The mechanical portion of this outside-framed locomotive was interesting in that the bonnet or engine compartment was built to the full width of the locomotive, allowing access walkways alongside

the engine, entered through doors in either side of the cab front from inside the driving cab; windows were fitted in the bonnet sides.

The locomotive was shipped to Antofagasta as deck cargo, and suffered some damage en route in a storm. After unloading and repairs, it had then to run some 700 miles over the Antofagasta, Chile & Bolivia Railway to reach La Paz. Hauling a train to accommodate the crew, the locomotive took a week to complete the journey over the mountainous route, which included altitudes of almost 13,000ft. Tests at La Paz showed that it could start a train on a radius curve of about 300yd and on a 1 in 14 gradient. This locomotive was probably the first successful high-altitude diesel locomotive in the world.

The granting in 1939 of the first two Buxton flameproof certificates for mining locomotives with diesel engines was an important event for the British locomotive industry. The first Buxton certificate was granted to Ruston & Hornsby, who completed their first locomotive in 1939 but did not manage to be the first to sell a certificated flameproof locomotive.

The second flameproof Buxton certificate was granted to the Hunslet Engine Co, who went ahead and actually built the first certified locomotive with a diesel engine to enter service in a British gaseous coal mine. Thus it was once again this Leeds company that made its mark in British diesel rail power.

The locomotive concerned (HE 2008/39) was a 2ft-gauge 0-4-0DM machine fitted with a Gardner 2L2 two-cylinder engine of 23hp at 1,300rpm. A Hunslet transmission and jackshaft and side-rod drive unit was fitted which provided speeds of 3, 4·66, 7·9 and 11·5mph. Weight in working order was 4 tons 11½cwt, and at 3mph the tractive effort was 2,450lb.

Hunslet 2008 went into service during July 1939 at Rossington Colliery, Yorkshire. Overall dimensions were: length 11ft 3½in, height 5ft, width 3ft 4in, wheelbase 3ft, wheel diameter 20in. Although this unit was the first to work in a coal mine, a similar Hunslet 'miner' preceded it when Hunslet 2001 was set to work at the Royal Navy Armament depot, Crombie, Fifeshire.

Following the 1937 example of the Southern Railway, the LMSR put in hand at Derby works a batch of diesel-electric shunting locomotives. Extensive trials with the two batches of ten locomotives by Hawthorn Leslie–English Electric and Armstrong Whitworth brought about a peculiar hybrid design from Derby.

The exact cause of this is a matter for conjecture, but by this time Armstrong Whitworth had gone out of the diesel traction market, thus leaving the way clear, or so it seemed, for English Electric to sweep the board with its design. However, this was not to be the case at first.

The Derby-built mechanical portion was based wholly on that of the Armstrong Whitworth type, but the power equipment was of English Electric manufacture, arranged in the locomotive to follow the Armstrong Whitworth layout. The engine was the English Electric type 6K, set to give 350hp at 685rpm. This drove the main generator, which in turn powered the single frame-mounted traction motor set above a geared jackshaft drive unit within the locomotive wheelbase, with side-rod drive. The control equipment was similar to Armstrong Whitworth's design, permitting speeds of 1mph to be steadily and continuously maintained on hump shunting operations, a feature of that manufacturer's locomotives.

Weighing 55¼ tons, the locomotive's tractive effort was 35,000lb, some 17 per cent more than the 1936 locomotives; the top speed was 20mph. Overall dimensions were: length 32ft 5½in, height 12ft 7in, width 8ft 7in, wheelbase 15ft 3in, wheel diameter 51in.

A total of four batches was ordered from Derby works between 1939 and 1942, comprising forty locomotives carrying LMSR stock Nos 7080–7119. During 1942, locomotives Nos 7100–09 were sold to the War Department and sent overseas. Some went to the Middle East, Nos 7100/1/2/4/7/8 being left when the British Suez bases were abandoned; Nos 7106/9 went to Africa where they first

worked on Tunisian Railways, and then, in 1946, joined Nos 7103/4 in Italy, where they were purchased to become Class 700, Nos 001–004 in Italian State Railways stock. The remainder became BR 12003–32 and were not withdrawn until 1966–7.

The locomotives served at all the main LMSR marshalling yards and hump yards, and were in later days allocated mostly to Crewe South, Speke Junction, Liverpool, Willesden, Toton, and Carlisle depots. Re-allocations took place as newer shunters were placed into traffic. Generally successful, frame troubles due to stresses set up by the final drive units were, however, said to be common.

During 1939–40 the Forth Banks, Newcastle upon Tyne, works of the merged Robert Stephensons & Hawthorn Company put in hand a development of the previous Hawthorn Leslie two-axle diesel mechanical shunter for use at government and military installations. These locomotives, closely following the design of HL 3949/50 for ROF Chorley, were built up to a total of twelve examples, carrying works Nos 6967/8/77–81/88–92. They had in some cases 137hp Crossley engines and in others 150hp Fowler–Sanders engines, a two-speed mechanical transmission with a top speed of 8mph, and jackshaft and side-rod drive.

These were the first diesel locomotives to carry the Stephenson name on their makers' plates, apart from the aforementioned English Electric units. Some of these were sold for industrial use after the run-down of military installations after the war and are still in existence.

The dispatch during April 1940 in wartime conditions of a large standard-gauge four-axle locomotive with mechanical transmission—the first eight-coupled rigid-framed diesel-engined locomotive ever built and sold by a British manufacturer—aroused considerable interest at the time. Built by the Hunslet Engine Co for the Trinidad Railways, which operated a 150 mile railway system with headquarters at Port of Spain, this was a 35 ton unit of conventional layout following Hunslet's usual design practice.

It carried works No 2016 of 1940 and was fitted with a Paxman–Ricardo six-cylinder engine of 275 hp at 1,000rpm. A Vulcan–Sinclair fluid coupling was fitted and a Hunslet auxiliary gear-change clutch, driving into a Hunslet patent four-speed gearbox with constant-mesh gears. The speed range was 5·37, 8·33, 12·22 and 18·44mph, final drive being by jackshaft and side rods. An auxiliary engine was fitted for starting the main engine, this being a Ford V8 petrol engine of 90hp at 4,000rpm. Maximum axle loading was 18 tons 16½cwt.

THE BRITISH INTERNAL-COMBUSTION LOCOMOTIVE: 1894-1940

The locomotive's overall length was 27ft 7½in, height 12ft, width 9ft, wheelbase 12ft 9in, wheel diameter 46in. Maximum tractive effort was 16,300 lb and the minimum curve negotiable was 300ft.

The period of World War II produced no very notable developments in British diesel railway traction. The bulk of the work in this field, mostly to government or military orders, comprised numerous shunters and small narrow-gauge units. The narrow-gauge types were mainly built by Motor Rail at Bedford, Ruston & Hornsby at Lincoln, and the Hunslet Engine Co at Leeds.

Standard-gauge diesel shunters were by John Fowler & Co, mainly 150hp 0–4–0 units for the Air Ministry, Royal Ordnance factories, etc. The Drewry Car Co, too, and Andrew Barclay, Sons & Co built a batch of 150hp shunters, the power equipment of which followed Drewry design practice, but was akin to Barclay's current work mechanically. These were mainly for the War Department. The Barclay order was executed at Kilmarnock, but the Drewry order was built both by E. E. Baguley at Burton-on-Trent and the Vulcan Foundry at Newton-le-Willows.

It was 1948 before the threads of mainline diesel locomotive production were picked up again, but that is another story and not to be pursued at this time.

APPENDIX

BUILDERS OF INTERNAL-COMBUSTION LOCOMOTIVES: 1894-1940

SIR W. G. ARMSTRONG, WHITWORTH & CO LTD
ENGINEERS AND SHIPBUILDERS
SCOTSWOOD-UPON-TYNE

Built locomotives from 1919, diesels introduced 1929, diesel department opened 1931–2. All locomotive work ceased 1939.

ASSOCIATED EQUIPMENT CO LTD
SOUTHALL (AEC)

Old-established road-vehicle builder. Built one locomotive in 1938.

AVONSIDE ENGINE CO LTD
AVONSIDE ENGINE WORKS, BRISTOL

Old-established locomotive builders. Built first internal-combustion locomotives in 1914. Closed down 1935, works sold. Goodwill and business purchased by Hunslet Engine Co Ltd.

W. G. BAGNALL LTD
CASTLE ENGINE WORKS, STAFFORD

Established 1875. First internal-combustion locomotives built 1914. Taken over by English Electric Co Ltd, 1961. Locomotive work ceased 1962.

E. E. BAGULEY LTD
ENGINEERS, BURTON-ON-TRENT

Traded as Baguley (Cars) Ltd, Baguley (Engineers) Ltd, E. E. Baguley Ltd, now as Baguley–Drewry Ltd. Built internal-combustion rail vehicles and locomotives from 1912, under McEwan Pratt, Baguley, and Drewry names. A few steam locomotives built in 1920s. Have carried out much subcontract work for other firms.

ANDREW BARCLAY SONS & CO LTD
CALEDONIA WORKS, KILMARNOCK

Established 1860. First internal-combustion locomotive built 1916. Now incorporates the locomotive businesses of North British Locomotive Co Ltd, and John Fowler & Co (Leeds) Ltd.

W. J. BASSETT-LOWKE LTD
MODEL ENGINEERS, NORTHAMPTON

Built one petrol-engined steam outline locomotive in 1909.

WILLIAM BEARDMORE & CO LTD
ENGINEERS, GLASGOW

Locomotive work started 1919. Some diesel locomotives built around 1930. Locomotive work ceased 1934–5. Beardmore oil engines built for rail traction purposes.

BIRMINGHAM SMALL ARMS CO LTD
SMALLHEATH WORKS, BIRMINGHAM

Traded as BSA. Built Drewry rail vehicles 1909–12. Locomotives proposed, but doubtful if any were built. Railway work ceased.

BLACKSTONE & CO LTD
ENGINEERS, STAMFORD

Built a few oil-engined locomotives during early 1920s. The firm now part of Lister–Blackstone group. Railway work ceased.

F. C. BLAKE & CO LTD
KEW, LONDON

Motor and motor-cycle makers. Built one locomotive in 1903. Closed down.

BRITISH THOMSON HOUSTON CO LTD
RUGBY

Traded as BTH. Designed and supplied power equipment for locomotives built by other manufacturers. Also acted as main contractors for a few diesel-electric locomotives. Now part of GEC–AEI–English Electric group.

J. W. BROOKE & CO LTD
ADRIAN IRONWORKS, LOWESTOFT

Built a motorcar with own engine and a few locomotives up to World War I. Now trade as Brooke Marine Ltd.

CROSSLEY BROTHERS LTD
ENGINEERS, MANCHESTER

Built a small number of locomotives with petrol engines during early 1920s in the works of Saunderson Tractor & Implement Co Ltd, Bedford, which they took over. Build diesel engines but not locomotives now.

DICK, KERR & CO LTD
PRESTON

In business as electrical engineers and constructed petrol-electric locomotives during 1914–18 period. In 1918 became part of English Electric Co Ltd, who built locomotives and railcars, etc, there from 1929. Still part of GEC–AEI–English Electric group but locomotive work ceased.

DREWRY CAR CO LTD
LONDON

Had works at Teddington 1906–9. BSA and Baguley built their products from 1909, and also the Dick Kerr works of English Electric Co Ltd from 1930. Now part of Baguley–Drewry Ltd and still engaged on railway work.

ENGLISH ELECTRIC CO LTD
LONDON

Formed 1918 by amalgamation of Dick, Kerr & Co Ltd, Preston; Phoenix Dynamo & Manufacturing Co Ltd, Bradford; Siemens Bros Ltd, Stafford; and Willans & Robinson Ltd, Rugby. Very little internal combustion work until 1934 when locomotives put into production, mainly with subcontractors supplying mechanical parts. Some locomotive work done by Dick Kerr works, Preston. Later absorbed Vulcan Foundry Ltd, Robert Stephenson & Hawthorns Ltd and W. G. Bagnall Ltd locomotive businesses. Locomotive building work very limited today due to increased use of subcontractors.

JOHN FOWLER & CO (LEEDS) LTD
ENGINEERS, LEEDS

Built steam locomotives from 1866. First petrol locomotive built 1923. Diesel locomotives followed. All locomotive work ceased 1969, this part of business being taken over by Barclays in 1969.

GENERAL ELECTRIC CO LTD
WITTON, BIRMINGHAM

Did not build any diesel locomotives but acted as main and subcontractors for many.

HARDY RAILMOTORS LTD
SOUTHALL

Formed out of Four Wheel Drive Motor Co Ltd (FWD). Built light petrol shunting units. Absorbed by AEC Ltd.

HARLAND & WOLFF LTD
ENGINEERS AND SHIPBUILDERS, BELFAST

Built diesel locomotives 1933–8 in small numbers using Harland & Wolff-built engines.

R. & W. HAWTHORN, LESLIE & CO LTD
FORTH BANKS WORKS, NEWCASTLE UPON TYNE

Did much early research in internal-combustion rail traction. Built locomotives from 1915 with petrol, and in later years diesel, engines, many in co-operation with English Electric. During 1937 amalgamated with Robert Stephenson & Co Ltd to form Robert Stephenson & Hawthorns Ltd.

F. C. HIBBERD & CO LTD
PARK ROYAL

Makers of Planet locomotives from 1926, at first using subcontractors to build them. Works opened 1932, closed 1963 and business moved to Butterley Co Ltd, Ripley, Derbyshire. Locomotive work practically ceased by 1971.

RICHARD HORNSBY & SONS LTD
GRANTHAM

Built a few oil-engined locomotives 1894–1903. Amalgamated to form Ruston & Hornsby Ltd, 1918.

J. & F. HOWARD LTD
BRITANNIA WORKS, BEDFORD

Built petrol locomotives from 1924. Works closed 1931. Locomotive business sold to F. C. Hibberd & Co Ltd, 1932.

ROBERT HUDSON & CO LTD
GILDERSOME FOUNDRY, MORLEY, LEEDS

Light railway engineers. Supplied internal-combustion locomotives of various makes plus a few of own type built by subcontractors. Still in business.

HUDSWELL, CLARKE & CO LTD
RAILWAY FOUNDRY, LEEDS

Established 1860. Built internal-combustion locomotives from 1925. Still in business as Hudswell–Badger Ltd.

HUNSLET ENGINE CO LTD
HUNSLET ENGINE WORKS, LEEDS

Established 1864. Built first diesel locomotives 1932. Absorbed Kerr, Stuart & Co Ltd, Avonside Engine Co Ltd in 1930 and 1935. Still very much in business.

JAMES C. KAY & CO LTD
PHOENIX FOUNDRY, BURY

Built a few petrol locomotives during late 1920s, early 1930s.

KENT CONSTRUCTION & ENGINEERING CO LTD
ASHFORD, KENT

Commenced locomotive work after World War I. Sold petrol locomotives under 'Planet' nameplate, sold by Honeywill Brothers Ltd, London. Works closed 1926, business taken over by F. C. Hibberd & Co Ltd.

KERR, STUART & CO LTD
CALIFORNIA WORKS, STOKE-ON-TRENT

Built internal-combustion locomotives from 1903, and from 1928 a standard range of diesel locomotives. Works closed 1930 and business taken over by Hunslet Engine Co Ltd.

KILMARNOCK ENGINEERING CO LTD
KILMARNOCK

Built one petrol locomotive in 1930 for Drewry Car Co Ltd. Works closed.

KITSON & CO LTD
AIREDALE FOUNDRY, LEEDS

Did work on Kitson–Still diesel steam locomotive from 1927. Firm ceased locomotive manufacture by agreement in 1938. Followed by eventual closure.

LAKE & ELLIOT LTD
BRAINTREE

Produced a petrol shunting tractor from early 1920s. No other railway work carried out.

R. A. LISTER & CO LTD
DURSLEY

Produced light petrol and later diesel locomotives from around 1926. Became part of Lister–Blackstone group. Locomotive work ceased 1970.

MANNING WARDLE & CO LTD
BOYNE ENGINE WORKS, LEEDS

Built a few petrol locomotives during 1915–20 period. Works closed down 1928.

MAUDSLAY MOTOR CO LTD
PARKSIDE WORKS, COVENTRY

Built one locomotive in 1902.

MCEWAN, PRATT & CO LTD
MURRAY WORKS, WICKFORD, ESSEX

In business from 1905/6 building internal-combustion locomotives, railcars, etc. Closed down 1914. Business taken over by Baguley (Cars) Ltd, 1914.

MOTOR RAIL & TRAM CAR CO LTD
SIMPLEX WORKS, BEDFORD

In business from 1911 at Lewes. Moved to Bedford and first locomotives built 1915. Still in business today as Motor Rail Ltd. Took over Ruston & Hornsby locomotive range 1966.

MUIR-HILL SERVICE EQUIPMENT LTD
TRAFFORD PARK

Mainly contractors' plant makers. Built petrol locomotives from 1926. Locomotive work ceased 1939/40.

NASMYTH, WILSON & CO LTD
BRIDGEWATER FOUNDRY, PATRICROFT

Built first petrol locomotive in 1911 and others during World War I. Works closed 1939.

CHARLES PRICE & SONS LTD
BROADHEATH

Mainly agricultural engineers but built a few small locomotives until around 1920. Closed down.

PRIESTMAN BROTHERS LTD
HULL

Built the world's first successful oil engines and the first oil-engined locomotive in 1894. No others ever built. Still in business as crane and excavator makers.

RANSOMES & RAPIER LTD
WATERSIDE WORKS, IPSWICH

Built a range of contractors' diesel locomotives from 1928 to 1939. Still in business as crane makers and engineers.

RUSTON & HORNSBY LTD
LINCOLN

Formed in 1918 by Richard Hornsby & Sons Ltd and Ruston & Proctor Ltd. Built a few locomotives in early 1920s, diesel range from 1932 until 1966 when locomotive work ceased and transferred to Motor Rail Ltd. Now part of GEC–AEI–English Electric group.

RUSTON & PROCTOR LTD
LINCOLN

Built a few locomotives during World War I. In 1918 amalgamated with Richard Hornsby & Sons Ltd to form Ruston & Hornsby Ltd.

SAUNDERSON & GIFKINS LTD
ELSTOW WORKS, BEDFORD

Built a few light locomotives before World War I. Became Saunderson Tractor & Implement Co Ltd. Works taken over by Crossley Brothers Ltd 1925.

STANDARD STEEL CO LTD
CROYDON

Mainly plant engineers and contractors' agents.

Built a few small locomotives from 1928, sold as 'Stansteco' locomotives. Locomotive work ceased. Now trade as Metal Propellors Ltd.

ROBERT STEPHENSON & HAWTHORNS LTD
DARLINGTON AND NEWCASTLE UPON TYNE

Formed 1937 by amalgamation of Robert Stephenson & Co Ltd and R. & W. Hawthorn, Leslie & Co Ltd. A few diesel locomotives built 1938–41, and from 1945. Became part of English Electric Co Ltd in 1955 and both works closed in 1960–4 period as part of a rationalisation programme.

STRAKERS & SQUIRE LTD
LONDON

Road vehicle makers. Built one locomotive in 1910. Closed down.

VULCAN FOUNDRY LTD
NEWTON-LE-WILLOWS

Established 1832. Built one diesel locomotive in 1934, and others from 1941. Taken over by English Electric Co Ltd in 1955. Locomotive work largely ceased by 1969 and now part of GEC–AEI–English Electric group.

D. WICKHAM & CO LTD
WARE

Railcar builders. Built a few locomotives 1928–36 period.

WOLSELEY MOTOR & TOOL CO LTD
BIRMINGHAM

Built only a few locomotives in early 1900s.

ACKNOWLEDGEMENTS

THIS book could not have been prepared at all without the assistance and contributions of the following, whose help is gratefully acknowledged: G. Arnott; V. J. Bradley; L. G. Charlton; T. D. A. Civil; A. R. Etherington; K. Hoole; G. Horsman; S. A. Leleux; W. Hewitson-Menzies; R. P. Morris; P. D. Nicholson; K. P. Plant; D. C. Plyer; R. N. Redman; M. Swift; C. R. Weaver; A. G. Wells; A. Wright; W. K. Williams; A. Wilson.

The following firms and their staff are thanked: Crossley Bros Ltd; Crompton Parkinson Ltd; Drewry Car Co Ltd; Harland & Wolff Ltd; F. C. Hibberd & Co Ltd; Hudswell Clarke & Co Ltd; Hunslet Engine Co Ltd; Muir-Hill Ltd; Priestman Bros Ltd; Ransomes & Rapier Ltd; Ricardo & Co Ltd; Sulzer Bros (London) Ltd; D. Wickham & Co Ltd; and the British Railways Board archives at York.

Similarly the officers and records of the following societies have been most helpful: Narrow Gauge Railway Society; Industrial Railway Society; Railway Correspondence & Travel Society; and Stephenson Locomotive Society.

ILLUSTRATIONS
THE majority of the illustrations are taken by or from the author's collection, others having been kindly supplied by the following, to whom the writer is indebted: P. S. Berridge, Fig 86; T. D. A. Civil, Figs 11, 90; Crossley Brothers Ltd, Fig 42; R. Etherington, Fig 64; John Fowler & Co (Leeds) Ltd, Fig 33; GEC Traction Ltd, Fig 58; F. C. Hibberd & Co Ltd, Fig 56; G. Horsman, Figs 6, 10, 23, 34, 46, 47, 48; Harland & Wolff Ltd, Figs 70, 91, 93; V. Nutton, Fig 84; Priestman Brothers Ltd, Fig 1; Ruston-Paxman Diesels Ltd, Figs 2, 5, 17, 33; Sulzer Bros (London) Ltd, Figs 49, 65, 73, 89; M. Swift, Fig 24.

INDEX

119